Study Guide and Activities

TO ACCOMPANY

Investigating the Social World

PINE FORGE PRESS TITLES OF RELATED INTEREST

Adventures in Social Research: Data Analysis Using SPSS® for Windows™ by Earl Babbie and Fred Halley

Adventures in Criminal Justice Research: Data Analysis Using SPSS® for Windows™ by George W. Dowdall, Earl Babbie, and Fred Halley

Critical Thinking for Social Workers: A Workbook by Leonard Gibbs and Eileen Gambrill

Exploring Social Issues Using SPSS® for Windows™ by Joseph F. Healey, Earl Babbie, and Fred Halley

Building Community: Social Science in Action edited by Philip Nyden, Anne Figert, Mark Shibley, and Darryl Burrows

The Pine Forge Press Series in Research Methods and Statistics
Edited by Kathleen S. Crittenden

- ***Investigating the Social World: The Process and Practice of Research*** by Russell K. Schutt

- *A Guide to Field Research* by Carol A. Bailey

- *Designing Surveys: A Guide to Decisions and Procedures* by Ronald Czaja and Johnny Blair

- *How Sampling Works* by Richard Maisel and Caroline Hodges Persell

- ***Social Statistics for a Diverse Society*** by Chava Frankfort-Nachmias

- *Experimental Design and the Analysis of Variance* by Robert Leik

- *Regression: A Primer* by Paul Allison

Study Guide and Activities

TO ACCOMPANY

Investigating the Social World

Russell K. Schutt

University of Massachusetts, Boston
Harvard Medical School

Pine Forge Press

Thousand Oaks, California ▪ London ▪ New Delhi

For information, address:

 Pine Forge Press
A Sage Publications Company
2455 Teller Road
Thousand Oaks, California 91320
(805) 499-4224
E-mail: sales@pfp.sagepub.com

Sage Publications Ltd.
6 Bonhill Street
London EC2A 4PU
United Kingdom

Sage Publications India Pvt. Ltd.
M-32 Market
Greater Kailash I
New Delhi 110 048 India

Production: Myrna Engler-Forkner, Rogue Valley Publications
Interior Designer: Lisa Mirski Devenish
Typesetter: Rebecca Evans
Cover Designer: Paula Shuhert and Graham Metcalfe
Production Manager: Anne Draus, Scratchgravel Publishing Services
Print Buyer: Anna Chin

Printed in the United States of America
97 98 99 00 01 10 9 8 7 6 5 4 3 2 1

ISBN 0-7619-8529-8

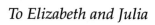

To Elizabeth and Julia

About the Author

Russell K. Schutt, Ph.D., is Professor of Sociology at the University of Massachusetts, Boston. He is the author of *Organization in a Changing Environment, Responding to the Homeless: Policy and Practice* (with Gerald R. Garrett) and numerous journal articles on organizations, law, homelessness, mental health, and teaching research methods. He was co-investigator on a federally funded experimental study of housing options for homeless mentally ill persons and, since 1990, has been a lecturer on sociology in the Department of Psychiatry at the Harvard Medical School.

About the Publisher

Pine Forge Press is a new educational publisher, dedicated to publishing innovative books and software throughout the social sciences. On this and any other of our publications, we welcome your comments and suggestions.

Please call or write us at:

Pine Forge Press
A Sage Publications Company
2455 Teller Road
Newbury Park, CA 91320
(805) 499-4224
E-mail: sales@pfp.sagepub.com

Visit our new World Wide Web site, your direct link to a multitude of on-line resources: http://www.sagepub.com/pineforge

Contents

Preface

This workbook offers a mix of questions and exercises to help you master the text within the available time. I have maintained the same goals for the workbook as for the text: integrating instruction in research methods with investigations of interesting social issues, improving your ability to evaluate research, and training you to actually do research. The workbook also is as comprehensive and up to date as the text, with many exercises using the 1994 General Social Survey and a guide to resources on the World Wide Web.

You will find material here that will help you no matter what the constraints on your time and irrespective of your particular learning style. The text objectives, short essay questions, and multiple-choice questions can all be used to review critical research concepts and prepare for exams. Summaries of newspaper stories engage you in interesting applications of social research to real-world problems. Mini-projects chart a direction for further exploration of research techniques. Finally, an annotated listing of World Wide Web sites guides you to the ever-expanding collection of worldwide resources available to social researchers.

I thank Professor Ron McAllister in the sociology department at Northeastern University for his very valuable comments, which helped to shape the final version of this workbook.

Workbook Overview

Each chapter begins with the outline of the corresponding text chapter and a list of chapter objectives. Set these objectives as your goals for studying, with whatever modifications or emphases your instructor announces. Each objective involves mastering some critical concept or technique. General Social Survey exercises illustrate methodological principles with statistical applications. Each one begins with the unstated phrase, "You will be able to."

The next section will help you to understand and remember the many new terms that you are encountering in the text. "Research in the News" illustrates the application of the chapter terms and techniques in real research studies on topics of current interest. Read each of these news summaries, and you will get a good idea of how particular research methods are applied to important social problems. Then answer the questions at the end of each news summary. These questions will help you to see different aspects of the potential for some of the research methods you are studying.

Answers to the short essay questions can be written in the book. Turn your answers in to your instructor for review, or use them as the basis of a class discussion about important terms and techniques. Multiple-choice questions will help you prepare for exams and force you to test your understanding of course material. Answers are at the end of this study guide.

Two to five mini-projects are outlined in each chapter. These projects require you to concentrate your attention on a subset of the most important research techniques. They usually provide some experience in searching and/or critiquing the literature as well as in designing and carrying out actual steps in the research process. You won't find any of the mini-projects boring. Most of them will be a lot of fun. But be sure to allow yourself enough time to write and review your findings before turning in a mini-project paper.

Your instructor may suggest that you work with a team of students in completing some of the mini-projects, which are well suited to a team effort. A little ingenuity on your part can ensure that the whole product of a team-based mini-project will be more than the sum of its parts.

Explorations with the 1994 General Social Survey make up the last section of most chapters. The GSS is included on the disk you received with the text. Just copy it to your personal computer's hard disk, and type GS in DOS (or in the DOS window from within Windows). Of course, you also have to have SPSS® for Windows™ installed on your computer's hard disk. If you or your college has SPSS® for Windows™, you're ready for some exciting investigations of the American people in 1994.

If you can access the World Wide Web on the Internet, you will also want to look over the annotated list of Web sites at the end of this study guide. Many on-line resources are available to help you search literature, find databases, and obtain grants.

Don't forget the exercises at the end of each chapter in the text. I have tried not to duplicate those exercises in this study guide, so they still provide additional suggestions for honing your research skills. Happy investigating!

■ ■ ■ ■   A few additional notes on the General Social Survey: You can obtain data from other years and variables from GSSDIR, the World Wide Web site described in the Web appendix. If you do use the GSS exercises (a very good idea), you should start with the exercises in chapter 1 and spend at least some time with each of the exercises in chapters 1–5. Each of these chapters introduces fundamental techniques that you will need to successfully complete GSS exercises in later chapters.

GSS first shifted from an annual to a biennial schedule in 1994. As a result, the GSS94 was a very large survey, with 2,992 respondents and 842 variables. In fact, the sample size and the number of variables were equivalent to what previously had been accomplished in two separate annual GSS efforts. Although I have omitted many variables to make the file fit on the accompanying disk, it still is very large, with 566 variables. You can use it to investigate many issues on your own.

If you have already completed a course in statistics, the GSS exercises will provide a good review of the basics. If you have not yet studied statistics, you may find some of the statistics terminology to be a bit obscure. Don't worry. This is not a statistics text. I use some statistics to illustrate important concepts in data analysis with the GSS, but you don't have to understand the formulas or even all the assumptions behind these statistics in order to understand my rather basic points. Consider your GSS exercises to be an easy way to gain some familiarity with the important concepts that you will study later in a formal statistics course.

1   Science, Society, and Social Research

■ ■ ■ ■ **Text Objectives**

1. Explain the motivations for social scientific research.

2. Define *social science* and distinguish it from nonscientific bases of authority.

3. Identify common errors in reasoning in popular discussions of social problems.

4. Give an example of each of the four types of social research questions: descriptive, exploratory, explanatory, and evaluative.

5. Elaborate on the theoretical implications of research proposals and reports.

6. Define *validity* and distinguish its three components: measurement validity, causal validity, and generalizability.

Research in the News

1. Concern with the decline of community is as old as the history of sociology itself. But the growing popularity of private, guarded communities in the United States poses some new questions about the meaning of the community ideal (Timothy Egan, "Many Seek Security in Private Communities." *The New York Times*, September 3, 1995: 1, 22). In 1995 it was estimated that close to 4 million Americans lived in closed, gated communities, with a total of 28 million in communities governed by a private association. Desires for predictable social rules, avoiding urban problems, maintaining safety, paying taxes only for one's own needs, and distrust of public government have each been cited as motivating the growth of these communities.

Propose a research project to study the growth of these communities that is descriptive, evaluative, explanatory, or exploratory. Suggest an explanation of the growth of these communities that is consistent with the social theorizing of Durkheim or of Marx. [13–23]

_____

_____

_____

_____

_____

_____

_____

_____

_____

_____

2. Small towns have been the traditional place where social scientists and others have looked to find the community ideal in practice. What do you think distinguishes the 16 million Americans (one-sixteenth of the population) who live in small towns (population under 10,000 and outside a metropolitan area) from those living in larger cities: Less likely to have parents born outside of the country? More likely to vote Republican, attend church, and support the death penalty? Less likely to be dependent on welfare? Less likely to have been beaten as children? More happily married?

According to an analysis of 1994 General Social Survey data reported in *The New York Times* (Sam Roberts, "Yes, a Small Town Is Different." August 27, 1995: E1, E5), the answers to the questions above are yes, yes, no, no, no. Are you surprised by any answers? To know that small town residents are more likely to be dependent on welfare, to have been beaten as children, and to report less marital happiness? What were your expectations based on: direct experience or others' statements? Had you made any errors in reasoning? Overgeneralizations? Illogical reasoning? What theoretical perspective has shaped your thinking about small towns in America? What general explanation could you propose to explain the findings reported by the *Times*? [6, 10–12, 119–21]

_____

_____

_____

_____

_____

_____

_____

_____

_____

_____

3. A report by the U.S. Justice Department revealed that the arrest rate for violent crime by juveniles age 10 to 17 increased by 100% between 1983 and 1992 (Fox Butterfield, "Grim Forecast Is Offered on Rising Juvenile Crime." *The New York Times,* September 8, 1995: A16). What do you think might explain this finding? What can be done to reduce this level of crime? More midnight basketball to provide an alternative activity?

It turns out that most of this juvenile crime occurs between 3 P.M. and 6 P.M.—after school but long before midnight basketball is available. Dean James Alan Fox of Northeastern University's college of criminal justice suggested that part of the reason for the increasing juvenile crime is the increasing absence of parental supervision after school due to two-earner families. More after school activities seemed likely to help.

What research project can you propose to evaluate the effect of after school programs on juvenile crime? If an association between after school programs and reductions in juvenile crime were found, what would you expect to limit the cross-population generalizability of the relationship? What would concern you in terms of achieving valid measures? How confident would you expect to be in the causal validity of your findings? Why? [23–28]

_____

_____

_____

_____

_____

_____

_____

_____

_____

_____

_____

Short Essay Questions

1. Some social scientists conduct research on corporate employees with the permission of the corporate board. Review the three motives for social research and discuss how they may each be relevant to such a research project. How might these motives create complementary and/or conflicting pressures on the researcher? Give hypothetical examples. [3–4]

_____

_____

_____

_____

_____

_____

_____

_____

_____

_____

_____

_____

_____

_____

_____

2. Using Exhibit 1.3 (text p. 21) as your guide, develop a comparable theoretical model of the generation of altruism. Then elaborate on this model, adding in a few other terms and arrows that identify some additional influences. Write a justification of your model. [21–23]

_____

_____

_____

_____

_____
_____
_____
_____
_____
_____

3. Write eight research questions about feelings of patriotism, with two questions for each of the four types discussed in the chapter: descriptive, exploratory, explanatory, and evaluative. [13–19]

_____
_____
_____
_____
_____
_____
_____
_____
_____
_____
_____

4. Write four propositions about the causes of acts of terrorism. Two propositions should reflect a Durkheimian theoretical perspective and two should reflect a Marxian theoretical perspective. Explain briefly why you think each proposition reflects the theoretical perspective. [22–23]

_____
_____
_____
_____
_____

_____

_____

_____

_____

_____

_____

_____

_____

_____

_____

5. A researcher asks five questions of a sample of community residents to find out how much they fear crime and whether their level of fear was influenced by a recent well-publicized murder in the community. Explain what the three dimensions of validity would refer to in this study and why they are important. [23–28]

_____

_____

_____

_____

_____

_____

_____

_____

_____

Multiple-Choice Questions*

1. The methods of social science are necessary in part because the self-interestedness of individuals can lead to an unwillingness to report honestly the results of social science studies. Other features of the social world identified as increasing the need for social science are human _____. [7–9]

    a. complexity, subjectivity, and resistance to change
    b. insufficient subjectivity as well as hyperobjectivity
    c. overconfidence, eagerness to change, and limited vision
    d. distorted personal and group experiences
    e. personal disinterestedness, objectivism, and resistance to change

2. Before Connie visits a small town, her friends tell her that small town people are closed minded. When she meets people at a small town picnic, she keeps her ears open for comments that seem to reflect a closed-minded unwillingness to entertain new ideas. She hears some remarks like this and concludes that her friends were correct. She has engaged in _____. [10–12]

    a. careful observation
    b. overgeneralization
    c. systematic reasoning
    d. inadequate generalizing
    e. selective observation

3. A car dealership that maintains an on-site play room for customers' kids must request renewed funding from the parent company. The company stipulates that the dealership show that its play room actually increases auto sales by customers who use it. What type of research is the dealership required to conduct? [13–17]

    a. descriptive
    b. exploratory
    c. explanatory
    d. evaluative
    e. selective

* The numbers that appear in brackets following multiple-choice questions are the text pages where this question is discussed.

4. A researcher studies recreational practices of recent immigrants. After he reports his findings, a community leader tells the researcher that many immigrants are unwilling to report their recreational practices because they believe others would think they did not work hard enough. This raises a question about _____. [24–28]

    a. cross-population generalizability
    b. measurement validity
    c. sample generalizability
    d. theoretical inconsistency
    e. causal validity

5. A researcher studies the effect of TV violence on marital conflict. She finds that spouses who have watched violent TV shows are more likely to have conflictual relations with their spouses than spouses who do not watch violent TV shows. However, she is hesitant to conclude that the violent TV shows increase marital conflict because she knows that spouses who watch violent shows are more likely to have conflictual styles of relating to others than spouses who do not choose to watch violent shows. What issue is she concerned with? [24–28]

    a. causal validity
    b. cross-population generalizability
    c. measurement validity
    d. sample generalizability
    e. theoretical inconsistency

6. A research team measures GPA and test anxiety in a sample of students in one school. They find that most of the students have high GPAs but still experience high levels of test anxiety. They present their findings to a group of teachers from schools throughout the state. Several teachers think that the findings would not hold at their schools. This thought is a challenge to the _____ of the findings. [24–28]

    a. cross-population generalizability
    b. measurement validity
    c. sample generalizability
    d. theoretical inconsistency
    e. causal validity

Mini-Projects

How Error Prone Is Popular Reasoning?

This project provides an estimate of the frequency with which errors are made in reasoning about individuals, societies, and social processes.

1. Collect seven issues of a daily newspaper. Locate the letters to the editor section in each.

2. Read each letter to the editor and circle all those that make assertions about individuals, societies, and social processes—that is, about the social world.

3. Identify examples of any of the four errors in reasoning in these letters. (Search through more newspaper issues, if necessary, until you find at least three examples of errors in reasoning about the social world.)

4. Speculate on the likelihood that the social world's complexity, self-interestedness, human subjectivity, or resistance to change resulted in each of the errors.

5. Rewrite the text of one of the letters to eliminate the errors in reasoning within it, but without changing the basic point of the letter.

6. Suggest two or more criteria that newspaper editors could use to spot errors in reasoning in the letters they are asked to publish.

How Popular Is Social Science?

What use is made of the results of social science research in the popular press?

1. Review one week's daily papers and check all those articles that report or refer to social science research results.

2. Calculate the proportion of *news* articles that take advantage of social science research.

3. Read each of the articles you checked. Indicate for each article the type of research involved (descriptive, evaluative, explanatory, or exploratory). Circle any statements in the articles that pertain to measurement, causality, or generalizability.

4. Summarize the information presented in each article about measurement validity, causal validity, and sample and cross-population generalizability.

5. Now grade each article on the basis of the extent to which information was provided with which to judge the validity of any statements made about measurement, causality, and generalizability. Use grades from 0 (failure) to 4 (excellent).

6. Describe your findings and review your conclusions in a short paper.

What Are Social Scientists Researching?

You are to focus on four issues of a social science journal, such as *American Sociological Review, American Journal of Sociology, Social Forces, Social Problems, Journal of Health and Social Behavior, Journal of Marriage and the Family,* or *Criminology.*

1. Count the number of articles involving empirical research in the four issues. Express this count as a percentage of the number of regular articles in these issues.

2. Create a coding matrix, in which the rows will represent journal articles and the columns will contain codes to indicate the type of research used (descriptive, evaluative, explanatory, or exploratory), the explicit use of any social science theory, and the name of the theory used. The coding matrix should also include columns in which to note the presence of any statements about measurement, causality, sample generalizability, or cross-population generalizability and whether any rationale was given for accepting the validity of these statements.

3. Code each of the articles in this matrix. In a footnote for each article, identify any errors that seem to have been made in reasoning.

4. Tally up your codes across the articles. Write a brief summary of what you have learned about the characteristics of research reported in these social science journals.

Altruism in Practice

Repeat the altruism study described in the text's Preface.

1. Select one of the techniques mentioned in the Preface to elicit altruistic behavior. Dropping the paper towels is certainly an easy one to use.

2. Team up with three other students. One student will serve as the aide, just standing off to one side ready to help in case a problem develops. The other two students are to be observers, counting the number of passersby who make an altruistic gesture.

3. Decide on what to count as altruistic gestures in response to the towel-dropping, or whatever technique you use. Also decide who should be omitted from the count (such as small children). You should practice the technique and try it out on a street corner before beginning the study.

4. Select a busy, safe sidewalk on a block where your actions will not interfere with businesses or with pedestrians who must cross a busy street or for other reasons must not be distracted.

5. The "stooge" should walk down the sidewalk, stumbling with the bag of towels, trying to find his or her way with a cane, or using whatever technique you have devised. He or she should turn the corner of the block and sit down or walk around the block or rest in a coffee shop or some such place for about 15 minutes. Then the process can be used again.

6. Observers should stand where they will not be noticed and where they will not interfere with the activity. One observer should count the total number of people passing by, and another observer should count the number of people who make an altruistic gesture.

7. Repeat the process several times over the course of one hour.

8. Find a place to sit down with your teammates to review the observers' notes and discuss the experience.

9. Write a report about your study. Describe what you have learned about altruistic behavior, review your methods, including your "experimental manipulation" (the technique to elicit altruistic behavior), your "sampling strategy" (the block(s) you selected and the types of people you counted), and your measures (the behaviors you counted as altruistic). Note any problems in using your methods and recommend improvements for future studies of this sort.

10. Discuss your findings in class and compare them to those of other student teams. How comparable were the methods used? Can the class identify any variation in altruism between locations used by different teams?

Exploring the General Social Survey

1. Investigate the structure of an SPSS system file. Look at the GSS data "spreadsheet" in SPSS for Windows. Each row of the data file corresponds to a particular respondent, whose respondent ID number appears in the first column. The columns of the data file reflect the questions in the survey; the mnemonic names that head each column give a rough idea of what the question was about. The numerical codes in the cells of the spreadsheet indicate how each respondent answered each question (and some codes indicate that the respondent was not asked or simply did not answer the question). For example, respondent 2 received a code of 1 for WRKSTAT, a code of 40 for HRS1, and a code of 0 for EVWORK. [493–495]

2. In order to learn more about the questions asked and the specific variables in the data file that reflect these questions, you can inspect the labels corresponding to each variable. You do this by clicking on the "Variable Info" button or pulling down the "Utilities" heading and selecting the "Variables" subhead. What you will see are the mnemonic names assigned to the GSS variables, short labels that summarize the corresponding survey questions, and the verbal labels and numerical codes assigned to each of the values of each variable (NAP means "not applicable," NA means "not answered," and DK means "don't know"). For example, the respondent with an ID of 1 received a code of 7 for WRKSTAT ("keeping house"), a code of –1 for hours worked last week (not applicable), and a 1 for ever worked (meaning he or she had worked in the past). Respondent 2's codes for these variables indicate that he or she works full time, 40 hours per week, and was not asked if he or she "ever" had worked as long as one year (EVWORK = 0).

You will quickly realize that there are too many variables to become familiar with, but you can begin to identify the subsets of variables that can be used to study different research questions. The subsets of variables usually appear sequentially in the file. For example, the first seven variables (WRKSTAT to INDUS80) concern the respondent's work status. Later in the data file you will find a set of variables dealing with formal political preferences (PARTYID to POLVIEWS).

Note that you can jump around in the variable list by using the slide bar or by typing the first letter of the name of the variable you want to find (and then pressing Enter). You can print out a list of all the variable and value labels by requesting "file info." (*Warning:* The complete list is 134 pages long.) [495–499]

3. Create a list of subsets of variables that you find to be of interest. There is no need to create a complete list at this time, but you should plan to expand this initial list as you spend more time with the data file. [499]

_____

_____

_____

_____

_____

_____

_____

4. Write four research questions, one corresponding to each of the four types of research questions introduced in chapter 1. Each research question should involve sets of variables that were included in the 1994 GSS. For example, one descriptive research question might be, "How much do Americans support government spending on different needs?" [13–19]

_____

_____

_____

_____

_____

_____

_____

_____

_____

2   The Process and Problems of Social Research

■ ■ ■ ■ **Text Objectives**

1. Write a social research question meeting the criteria of feasibility, social importance, and scientific relevance.

2. Find appropriate research references on a social scientific topic.

3. Distinguish deductive, inductive, and descriptive research and explain their role in the scientific process.

4. Apply scientific and ethical guidelines for social research to specific research proposals and projects.

Research in the News

1. What predicts the level of education that students complete? Can you think of some possible influences?

A study by the National Opinion Research Center at the University of Chicago, under contract to the United States Department of Education, gave some answers ("Income Found to Predict Education Level Better Than Race." *The New York Times*, June 17, 1996: A11). Social scientist Allen Sanderson tracked 25,000 teenagers from 1988, when they were in eighth grade, to 1994, when those who had gone to college were sophomores. He used several methods to ensure success in finding students for follow-up interviews.

Sanderson examined the ability of family income, race, ethnicity, gender, and scores on elementary school achievement tests to predict educational status after these six years. Family income proved to be most important: 74% of students from the most affluent families attended four-year colleges or universities, compared to 37% of those from the least affluent families. Students from different racial and ethnic backgrounds or of different genders did equally well in terms of college attendance, if they came from affluent families.

What type of research question was being investigated? What else would you like to know about the study to evaluate the causal conclusions? Was this deductive or inductive research? What might one hypothesis have been? What was one empirical generalization? How confident are you that family income is a key cause of college attendance? Would you agree with Sanderson's conclusion that adequate financial aid could give low-income students equal access to higher education? Is this policy recommendation derived directly from the study findings? [13–19, 43–52]

_____

_____

_____

_____

_____

_____

_____

_____

_____

_____

_____

_____

2. What consequences does divorce have for children? Research finds that children who have experienced the divorce of their parents are more likely to quit high school, have early sexual experiences, be unemployed, and get divorced themselves.

University of Texas sociologist Norval Glenn concludes from the evidence that "There are more serious consequences than we used to think," while University of Pennsylvania sociologist Frank F. Furstenberg, Jr., has a different emphasis: "The long-term effects of divorce are certainly there, but they're not quite as marked as one believes when you take into account what these marriages might have been like if these people had stayed married." (Irene Sege. "Adult Offspring of Divorce Struggle for a New Path." *Boston Globe,* December 26, 1995: 1, 22).

Several children of divorced parents recounted their experiences in the same article that reported this academic debate. One woman was 13 when her parents divorced. She recalled that it seemed to be "the beginning of the end for me." She became "uncontrollable" within two years of losing her father, quit high school, had two children without marrying, and went on welfare. Later, though, she returned to school and earned a master's degree in education.

What is the research question here? Does it meet each of the three criteria for a good social research question? Have you seen what you consider to be effects of divorce on children? If, as psychologist Judith Wallerstein remarked in the news article, "there's nothing written in the stars" about the effects of divorce on any particular child, what variables would you suggest should be considered to account for the ability of some children to manage in spite of experiencing divorce? Can you think of an alternative explanation for the differences in outcomes for children who experienced divorce and those who came from intact two-parent families? [35–38]

_____

_____

_____

_____

_____

_____

_____

_____

_____

3. "While times have changed, the [U.S.] Labor Department's statistical tools haven't," Louis Uchitelle explained in an article about "How the Job Count Is Off" (*New York Times*, November 7, 1993: E3). What is the problem? The Labor Department's measure of unemployment, developed in the 1940s, assumes that people with jobs are likely to stay in those jobs and that those who are not looking for work are not interested in working. It counts as unemployed those who have been out of work but looking for a job in the previous week.

Instead, Uchitelle suggested that today's reality is that there is a large group of men in their 40s and 50s who have given up looking for work and have retired. Many people who have been laid off from highly paid jobs accept poorly paid part-time jobs just to stay employed. And former white-collar employees have become a large component of the ranks of the unemployed.

If the "unemployment rate" as calculated in 1993 had taken into account part-time workers as well as people who were too discouraged to look for work, the unemployment rate would have been 10.2 rather than 6.8 percent—quite a difference.

What type of research question is this? What are the variables? What is an example of an empirical generalization? On what portion of the research circle does this research focus? What are the advantages and disadvantages of maintaining consistency in measurement as compared to making changes to adjust to developments in the social world? [13–19, 43–52]

_____

_____

_____

_____

_____

_____

_____

_____

_____

_____

_____

Name: _____ **Date:** _____ **Instructor:** _____

Short Essay Questions

1. Write three different social research questions: one that reflects your own interests, one that reflects an opportunity that you could take advantage of, and one that reflects what your studies suggest is a logical extension of prior research. Which social research question do you think you would best be able to study? Why? [35–38]

_____

_____

_____

_____

_____

_____

_____

_____

_____

_____

2. What research do you believe would be worthwhile on the value of midnight basketball and other city-sponsored sports activities for reducing urban crime? Propose in separate paragraphs a deductive research project, an inductive research project, and a descriptive research project. Explain why each project would be worthwhile. [35–38, 43–52]

_____

_____

_____

_____

_____

_____

_____

_____

_____

_____

_____

_____

_____

_____

_____

_____

_____

_____

_____

3. Is deductive research preferable to inductive research? In your answer, weight the pros and cons of both deductive and inductive research approaches. [45–52]

_____

_____

_____

_____

_____

_____

_____

_____

4. Prioritize the nine scientific guidelines in terms of their importance for successful social science research. Now order the guidelines in terms of what you think is the degree of difficulty for researchers in adhering to each one. Justify both sets of rankings. [53–56]

_____

_____

_____

_____

_____

_____

_____

_____

_____

_____

_____

_____

_____

_____

_____

_____

_____

5. Prioritize the five ethical guidelines in terms of their importance for ethical treatment of human subjects. Now order the guidelines in terms of what you think is the degree of difficulty for researchers in adhering to each one. Justify both sets of rankings. Which ethical guidelines interfere the most with adherence to particular scientific guidelines? [59–62]

_____

_____

_____

_____

_____

_____

_____

_____

Multiple-Choice Questions

1. A sociology professor evaluates different possible research questions. He reviews previous research on social class and religious commitment as well as on color preference and clothing style. He decides to focus on a research question involving color preference and clothing style. Which guideline for good research questions did he violate? [35–37]

    a. feasibility
    b. cost-effectiveness
    c. nonintrusiveness
    d. social importance
    e. scientific relevance

2. According to labeling theory, calling a person a deviant increases the likelihood that he or she will engage in deviant acts. A researcher decides that it is therefore likely that elderly people who are called senile will be more likely to act senile as a result. This is an example of _____. [43–47]

    a. expository reasoning
    b. deductive reasoning
    c. an empirical generalization
    d. inductive reasoning
    e. positivism

3. A researcher's careful observation reveals that soccer fans who become the most belligerent toward members of the other side have the weakest social ties in the community. She speculates that the intensity of feelings among sports fans compensates for a lack of opportunities for positive emotional expression in daily life. This speculation is an example of _____. [43–47]

    a. expository reasoning
    b. deductive reasoning
    c. an empirical generalization
    d. inductive reasoning
    e. positivism

4. A researcher hypothesizes that "The more interesting the task, the less the level of perceived stress." The dependent variable in this hypothesis can be stated most clearly as _____. [45]

    a. the more interesting the task
    b. degree of task interest
    c. stress
    d. level of perceived stress
    e. type of stress

5. A researcher hypothesizes that "Veterans are more likely to be patriotic than nonveterans." The independent variable in this hypothesis can most clearly be stated as _____. [45]

    a. likelihood of patriotism
    b. veterans
    c. level of patriotism
    d. veteran status
    e. more likely to be patriotic

6. What is the independent variable in this hypothesis: "College GPA increases with regularity of studying"? [45]

    a. college GPA
    b. regularity of studying
    c. studying
    d. college GPA increases
    e. amount of studying

7. Which of the following statements is *not* a hypothesis? [45]

    a. Social harmony increases with average literacy level.
    b. Reliance on physical punishment is more frequent the greater the perceived social distance between criminal and victim.
    c. High school graduates tend to read less frequently than college graduates.
    d. Texans are very assertive.
    e. Disease rates are higher in warmer than in colder climates.

8. Which of the following is *not* a variable? [45]

    a. shelter
    b. ethnicity
    c. conflict level
    d. state
    e. city size

9. A researcher measures the crime rate and the dispersion of incomes in a sample of communities. Based on her findings, she reports that there is no relation between the dispersion of incomes in these communities and their crime rate. This report is _____. [47]

    a. an empirical generalization
    b. a valid deduction
    c. a selective observation
    d. an overgeneralization
    e. an illogical conclusion

Mini-Projects

Identifying Good Research Questions

Formulating a good research question is one of the most difficult steps for many new social scientists. It's often not until after many false starts and dead ends that a worthwhile and feasible question emerges. And it's often not a whole lot easier for seasoned investigators. This project will give you an overview of the process and perhaps some tips to use in formulating your own research questions.

1. Identify a local social research organization, such as a survey research center at a university, the research department of a government agency, or a private social research firm. Or find a professor on your campus who has been active in social research. Ask your instructor for some suggestions.

2. Plan how you will ask an organizational representative, or the professor, for a 30-minute interview about his or her research experiences. Call and make arrangements.

3. Prepare an interview plan, including a very brief introduction of yourself and the reason for the interview as well as some background questions about the organization and your informant's job. The interview should focus primarily on the respondent's experiences with formulating research questions and reviewing those formulated by others.

4. Ask the respondent to list the research questions he or she currently is seeking to answer. You may also choose to ask about particularly interesting research questions the respondent has investigated in the past. Then ask the respondent how he or she selected each question.

5. Now ask your respondent to reflect on the quality of each research question. What questions proved to be feasible, socially important, and scientifically relevant? Which questions did your respondent end up changing (or wishing he or she had changed)?

6. What suggestions can your respondent make to help you avoid poor research questions?

7. Write up a short report on what you have learned about the process of formulating good research questions.

How Cumulative Is Social Science?

In this project you will trace the history of research on some problem and evaluate its consistency. This is to parallel, in a general way, the text presentation of the studies on the police response to domestic violence.

1. Propose several research questions to explore. Your goal is to pick just one of these questions that has been investigated in multiple studies. Make a quick check of *Soc. Abstracts* to determine which of your research questions seems to have been the focus of a body of research. Some good possibilities are: What is the effect of arrest (or incarceration) on recidivism? What influences levels of depression? Does social support affect the likelihood of physical illness (or recovery from illness)? What is the impact of race (or gender) on rates of pay?

2. Find a recent journal article on the selected question that reports the results of original research. Read the article. Summarize the research by noting the theoretical framework, the hypotheses tested, the dependent and independent variables, and the empirical generalizations about the findings. Note examples of deductive and inductive reasoning in the article (including discussions of anomalous or serendipitous findings).

3. Through reading the article (primarily the initial literature review and the concluding sections) and checking its bibliography, find previous research that focused on the same research question, with similar hypotheses. Copy the references to two such articles (focusing on articles that are in journals that you have access to).

4. Now read the two selected articles and summarize them both, as in step 2.

5. Repeat step 3 with your two new articles, but identify just one citation of a previous, related research article from each.

6. Repeat step 4.

7. You should now have summarized five articles that attempted to answer your research question. Write a short paper that evaluates the consistency of research about this question. How cumulative has this research been? Were any of the research studies explicit attempts to replicate the findings of an earlier study? Have there been any unanticipated findings in the studies you have learned about? Do you have a sense of researchers building on each other's work, or just going off in multiple directions?

8. Describe the points about which consensus has been reached and/or about which there is continuing controversy. What type of study might help to resolve one of these points of contention?

How Institutional Review Boards Work

Every institution of higher education that sponsors federally funded research on human subjects must have an institutional review board (IRB). What better way to learn about ethics in real research than through IRB members?

1. Obtain a list of IRB members from a university grants officer. You should speak to the IRB chair about your project and receive his or her permission before contacting any other IRB members. You may supplement the current IRB listing with names of past members.

2. Obtain from the IRB chair pertinent documents describing the responsibilities and mode of functioning of the IRB.

3. Call a current or former IRB member and ask for an interview for your class project.

4. Plan several questions about the review process. These might include the standards that are used in the review process, the relative difficulty of the ethical issues posed by proposals in different disciplines, and the features of proposals that have proven controversial in the course of decision making.

5. Conduct a half-hour interview about these issues. Be sure to thank the IRB member for her or his time.

6. Write a short paper reporting on the operation of an IRB and reviewing the ways in which different human subjects procedures have been evaluated.

Exploring the General Social Survey

1. Review the GSS research questions you proposed in the previous chapter. Revise or replace them, if necessary, so that they meet the three criteria for good research questions. Select your explanatory research question for a more intensive focus. Or select two research questions, because you might find later that it makes sense to shift your focus.

2. Search the literature for research articles on your research question that have used GSS data. The easiest way to do this is to access the GSS site on the World Wide Web. The homepage is at http://www.icpsr.umich.edu/gss/ (see the Web appendix in this workbook). Once there, you can search a list of GSS publications about similar topics and/or using the same variables.

3. Read and summarize several relevant articles. Try to identify the specific GSS variables used in the analyses and see if these variables are available in the 1994 GSS data file.

4. Review the original wording of the questions and response choices for the variables related to your research question. You can do this on the Web site, just by specifying the name of the variable(s) in which you are interested. Alternatively, your instructor can order a copy of the original 1994 GSS interview schedule or a codebook for the survey. Was the meaning of each question clear from the labels in the SPSS file? Does the actual wording of the questions and response choices make sense to you? Why or why not?

5. Did any questions related to your research question require special attention to protect the research subjects? Discuss in class any ethical issues that you feel are raised by any questions.

6. Formulate at least two hypotheses related to your research question, using specific 1994 GSS variables as the independent and dependent variables.

3 Conceptualization and Measurement

■ ■ ■ ■ **Text Objectives**

1. Define a concept and distinguish multiple dimensions of it.

2. Operationalize a concept using available data, single questions, a multi-dimensional index, and observations.

3. Know when open-ended and closed-ended questions are most appropriate in a survey.

4. Propose indicators for the same variable at different levels of measurement and with different units of analysis.

5. Evaluate procedures to test the reliability and validity of measures.

Research in the News

1. Social scientists at Fordham University's Institute for Innovation in Social Policy devised an index of "social health" ("U.S. Social-Health Index Dips, Scientists Say," *The New York Times*, October 15, 1995).

The index combines indicators of 16 different social problems, including child abuse, the gap between rich and poor, children living in poverty, number of uninsured, teenage suicide, and low weekly earnings. Each indicator, and the overall index, ranges from 0 to 100, based on its relation to the "least harmful" score ever recorded.

For the period between 1970 and 1993, the social health index was at its peak in 1973 (its score was 77.5) and reached a low of 38.1 in 1991. In recent years, the social health index has been falling even though the nation's Gross Domestic Product (GDP, the output of all goods and services) has been rising.

What components would you suggest for such a social health index? What about for an index of social health on your campus? [82–85]

2. "Shifting Public Opinion by a Turn of Phrase" was an apt title for a story about political polling in 1995 (Elizabeth Kolbert, *The New York Times*, June 5, 1995: A1, B6). It turns out that two questions that seem very similar yield very different results: "If Americans are asked whether they favor 'balancing the Federal budget,' more than two-thirds will say 'yes.' But if they are asked whether they favor balancing the budget if it means 'cuts in Medicare,' roughly the same proportion will say 'no.'"

How would you interpret this finding? What does it tell us about public opinion concerning the federal budget and Medicare? Can you think of a better way to measure level of support for balancing the budget? [79–82]

_____

_____

_____

_____

_____

_____

_____

_____

_____

3. Do you ever notice how people in a group react to someone else who is speaking? Smiling or frowning? Fidgeting or being attentive? Looking happy or unhappy? Psychologist Florence Geis systematically measured such reactions in a study of the extent of gender bias in the workplace ("Studies find workplace still a man's world," *Boston Globe*, March 12, 1990: 39, 41). The results were not encouraging for efforts to lessen bias.

"Not only are men and women in a group situation more likely to respond to female leaders with scowls and frowns, while smiling and nodding at male leaders who say the same thing. But the female leaders also invariably receive poorer evaluations than their male counterparts do."

Does this seem to be a reasonable approach to measure reactions to bias? Can you specify the procedures that should be followed? Can you expand on the list of behaviors to be observed? What test for reliability could you design? How would you go about assessing validity? [85–87, 96–100]

_____

_____

_____

_____

_____

_____

_____

_____

_____

_____

_____

_____

_____

_____

_____

_____

Short Essay Questions

1. Propose a conceptual definition of *political participation* that encompasses voting, political contributions, joining a political party, and any other behaviors that seem appropriate. Explain why you prefer this definition and why you included, or left out, particular behaviors. [71–75]

_____

_____

_____

_____

_____

_____

_____

_____

_____

_____

_____

2. You must devise survey questions to measure the level of support for state welfare policies. What issues should you consider in deciding whether to write open-ended or closed-ended questions? [79–82]

_____

_____

_____

_____

_____

_____

_____

_____

_____

_____

3. What are the advantages and disadvantages of using single questions rather than multidimensional index scores to measure concepts? [79–85]

_____

_____

_____

_____

_____

_____

_____

_____

_____

4. You must develop a measure of family conflict (families are the units of analysis). Propose measurement procedures using available data, questions, and observations. Discuss the advantages and disadvantages of these three measurement approaches. [75–88]

_____

_____

_____

_____

_____

_____

_____

_____

_____

_____

_____

_____

_____

_____

_____

_____

5. Propose measures of text anxiety at the nominal, ordinal, and interval or ratio levels. Write out the questions and response choices. Now specify one measure of text anxiety in which *groups* are the units of analysis. Which measure do you prefer and why? [88–95]

_____

_____

_____

_____

_____

_____

_____

_____

_____

_____

_____

_____

_____

_____

6. Social support can be measured with a series of questions that ask respondents whether they have someone they can depend on when they need a loan, when they want to talk about personal problems, when they need a ride to town, and so on. The social support measure is then the sum of responses to these questions. Propose a criterion validation procedure, a construct validation procedure, and a procedure for establishing the reliability of such a social support measure. Compare the advantages and dis-

advantages of the criterion and construct validation approaches and explain how the results of your evaluation of the index's reliability will affect your conclusion about its validity. [96–100]

_____

_____

_____

_____

_____

_____

_____

_____

_____

_____

_____

_____

_____

_____

_____

_____

_____

_____

Multiple-Choice Questions

1. Harvey Terpin wrote a proposal to study the impact of stress on levels of anxiety. One of his first steps was to review the meaning of *anxiety* in several social theories. Based on this review, he formulated his own definition of *anxiety*. This illustrates the process of _____. [69–75]

    a. operationalization
    b. validation
    c. conceptualization
    d. syllogistic reasoning
    e. reification

2. Which of the following is *not* a variable? [69–70]

    a. social class
    b. the capitalist system
    c. the extent of discrimination
    d. country of origin
    e. instructional method

3. A researcher defines social support as the receipt from others of emotional, material, or intellectual resources. She devises a survey to indicate the level of social support among a sample of hospital patients. Her survey consists of 10 questions, each of which asks whether the respondent has received a specific type of resources from others. She counts the number of affirmative responses to serve as her indicator. This count is an example of _____. [69–75]

    a. conceptualization
    b. operationalization
    c. validation
    d. verification
    e. reification

4. Survey respondents are asked how much social support they receive from family members, neighbors, business acquaintances, and other friends. Their responses to each question are scored on a scale from 1 to 5 and then these scores are added together. The result is _____. [69, 82]

    a. a concept
    b. an index
    c. triangulation
    d. secondary data
    e. a field note

5. A closed-ended survey question is _____. [79]
   a. one that has explicit, fixed response choices
   b. one whose meaning is not open to equivocation
   c. actually a statement rather than a question
   d. one that respondents answer in their own words
   e. rarely used in mailed surveys

6. A researcher concludes that a self-esteem measure is valid after she finds that it varies in relation to feelings of mastery, internal locus of control, social support, and number of group memberships. What approach to validity is she relying on? [96–99]
   a. content validity
   b. criterion validity
   c. concurrent validity
   d. construct validity
   e. predictive validity

7. The relation between measurement reliability and validity is that _____. [96–100]
   a. an invalid measure cannot be reliable
   b. a conclusion that a measure is valid implies nothing about its reliability
   c. neither can be determined unless the sample is representative
   d. a valid measure must be a reliable measure
   e. a reliable measure must be a valid measure

8. The strategy of asking questions is particularly well suited to measuring attitudes or behaviors that are _____. [87]
   a. socially stigmatized
   b. readily observable
   c. rationales for taking actions
   d. quantifiable
   e. very socially desirable

9. A researcher studies patient satisfaction with health care delivery. She surveys patients discharged from 105 hospitals in 22 cities, using a questionnaire that asks patients how satisfied they are with the health care they received (with the responses scored from 1 to 5). She then examines the relationship between patient satisfaction and the proportion of their hospital bill covered by insurance. She finds that the higher the proportion of their hospital bill covered by insurance, the more satisfied the patients. Her units of analysis were _____. [88–90]

a. individuals
b. hospitals
c. cities
d. individuals and hospitals
e. hospitals and cities

10. In a study of publications in criminology, the variable "article quality" is measured by asking criminologists to rate the publications on a scale from 1 to 5, where 5 = excellent, 4 = good, 3 = average, 2 = poor, and 1 = very poor. The level of measurement of "article quality" is _____. [90–95]

a. nominal
b. ordinal
c. interval
d. ratio
e. dichotomy

11. Which of the following is a property of a variable measured at the nominal level? [90–92]

a. fixed zero point
b. constant measurement units
c. ordered values
d. overlapping categories
e. exhaustive categories

12. A college career counselor administers a test of students' preferences for jobs involving quantitative skills to all participants in a college job fair. Each student's quantitative preferences are scored from 0 to 100. The fair organizer then tallies the number of jobs involving quantitative skills for which each student interviewed at the job fair. He then compares students' preference scores to the proportion of jobs for which they interviewed that involved quantitative skills. This is an example of _____ validity. [96–99]

a. content
b. face
c. concurrent
d. construct
e. predictive

13. Executive secretaries are asked in a survey how often they correct spelling errors in the material their boss gives them to type. The survey is repeated with the same secretaries on five consecutive days. The secretaries' answers are consistent across this time period, but a careful before–after comparison of the original handwritten documents with the secretaries' typed versions indicates that the secretaries correct spelling errors much

less frequently than their survey answers had indicated. This suggests that the question-based measure of the frequency of secretarial correction of bosses' spelling errors is _____. [96–100]

    a. reliable but not valid

    b. valid but not reliable

    c. neither reliable nor valid

    d. reliable and valid

    e. valid on its face but not in its content

Mini-Projects

Each of the mini-projects can be completed on your own or with a group of classmates. Review the relevant chapter sections before attempting to carry out the project.

Evaluating an Attitudinal Measure

This project is to provide some insight into how to evaluate an attitudinal measure. You could focus on the CES-D depression index (Exhibit 3.4, text p. 83) or find another index in a journal article or a social science book.

1. Select a short index used to measure some attitude of interest to you.

2. Evaluate the validity of the index "on its face"—that is, using a content validity approach. Identify any component dimensions and consider whether the index in fact covers the relevant dimensions.

3. Select two to three readily available people to whom you can administer the index. These could be classmates or other friends, coworkers, family members, or neighbors. Ask these people to complete the index and then review their answers with them. Read each question and ask what they had in mind as they answered the question. Record their explanations.

4. Review the answers and write up a critique (positive, negative, or mixed) of the index.

Designing an Attitudinal Measure

You are to design two measures of an attitude and collect some pilot data. Work with a small group of classmates for this project.

1. Identify an attitudinal concept that is of interest to you and could be operationalized with measures in a student survey.

2. Identify a variable related to this concept and write one question with which to measure it. Also compose a set of mutually exclusive and exhaustive response choices—four response choices for each question.

3. Exchange these questions and response choices within your group. Review and compare each question and its response choices. Eliminate questions that are too similar or that do not appear to measure the concept. If the concept seems to have multiple dimensions, consider whether to try to measure each dimension or whether to focus instead on just one dimension.

4. Select about 10 questions to include in an index to measure the concept. Also identify one single question that provides a general measure of the concept.

5. Type the questions and response choices on one page. Duplicate for administration to another class and make arrangements to administer the instrument in one class.

6. Distribute the set of questions to students in the selected class by arrangement with the instructor. Collect during the same class session and tally up the responses to each question.

7. Calculate an index score for each student by adding up the scores on responses to the index questions. Tally up scores on this index and on the single-question measure.

8. Compare the distribution of index scores and of responses to the single-question measure. How similar are these distributions? How consistent were responses to the questions included in the index? Which measurement approach do you have more confidence in at this point, single questions or an index? Explain your answer.

Seeing Is Believing

This project is designed as a first experience in measurement through observing.

1. Identify a public place where there are a number of people whom you can observe for a while without being conspicuous. Possibilities include train, plane, bus, or subway terminals, shopping malls, downtown street corners, museums, or sports arenas.

2. Specify one or more behaviors of interest in this setting, such as displays of affection, acknowledging strangers, walking speed.

3. Develop a measurement procedure for this behavior. This may take the form of counting specific behaviors or describing the quality of social interaction. In either case, develop a form on which to record your observations.

4. Spend 30 minutes observing and recording your observations of the behavior(s) of interest.

5. Describe what you observed, including a summary of variation in the behavior(s) you measured. Did you feel that you were measuring what you intended to measure? Did you feel you were missing any important aspects of variation in the behavior of interest because of the way you designed your measurement procedure?

Media Content

In this project you will develop measures of the content of TV programs. You could team up with two or three other classmates for this project. In most instances it will help to focus your attention on one type of programming (news, soap operas, children's programs, serials, sports, and so on).

1. Identify a concept(s) of interest that could be operationalized with the content of TV programs. Some possibilities are interpersonal violence, gender bias, police roles, stereotypes, or family interaction.

2. Specify specific variables that reflect these concepts in the context of TV programs—for example, "frequency of arguments" to measure family conflict or "number of intentionally inflicted deaths or injuries by others" to measure interpersonal violence.

3. Develop a specific measurement procedure that operationalizes each concept. By this point you should be thinking in terms of specific TV programs. An example for "frequency of arguments" would be "count the number of arguments between family members in each program or episode, with one argument represented by the period between the start of angry vocalizations or abusive treatment and ending when these behaviors subside." Prepare a grid for recording scores for each measure and each program.

4. Try out the measure(s) with one or two TV programs, note any problems, and revise the measurement procedure(s) if necessary.

5. Now code four hours of TV programs, noting any additional problems with the measurement procedures.

6. Report on the distribution of scores on your measure(s). Review any measurement problems you have identified and suggest improvements in the measurement instrument.

Exploring the General Social Survey

1. Identify GSS variables measured at the nominal, ordinal, and ratio levels. You can do this by scrolling through the pull-down variable list. Start this search with variables related to your research question. Write out the variable labels and the labels corresponding to each of the numerical values. Justify your classification of each variable's level of measurement. You can check yourself by seeing if you understand why I have classified these variables as follows: WRKSTAT is measured at the nominal level, POLVIEWS at the ordinal level, HRS1 at the ratio level, and WRKSLF is a dichotomy. [90–95]

_____

_____

_____

_____

_____

_____

_____

2. Now note carefully the correspondence between each variable's numerical values (codes) and the labels that indicate the meaning of these values. Is there an intrinsic order to the values, as labeled? Is this order reflected in the numerical codes assigned to those values? [90–95]

_____

_____

_____

_____

_____

_____

_____

3. You will find that sometimes the numerical codes assigned to values do not correspond to the intrinsic order of the values. It is very important to notice this and to reorder the values before you analyze your data. The SPSS program takes account only of the order of the numerical codes, so if the numerical response codes for a variable measured at the ordinal level do not correspond to the intrinsic order of the values, the variable is in effect not measured at the ordinal level.

Don't be confused by missing values, however. When respondents do not answer a question, they are given a special code that is then designated as a missing value. These appear in the variable list with the letter *M*. Cases with missing values on a particular variable are not included in statistical calculations involving that variable, so you don't need to worry about the numerical codes for the missing values being "out of order."

Let's return to the problem of valid values that are assigned numerical codes that do not correspond to their intrinsic order. An example will clarify the problem. Find the variable NATSPAC in the variable list. Its values range from 1 to 3, corresponding to "too little," "about right," and "too much." No problem there, right? Now check on the variable COURTS. Again there are three values, coded from 1 to 3. But now the labels of these values, in the order in which they were coded, are "too harsh," "not harsh enough," and "about right." The middle response, "about right," has a numerical code that is higher than what is actually the highest value, "not harsh enough." This means that the variable, which was actually measured at the ordinal level, will not function as an ordinal variable in the analysis until we fix the codes.

You can change the correspondence of numerical codes and value labels with RECODE (an SPSS command). Although this can be done through the pull-down EDIT menu, you can do it with command syntax. To use command syntax, just pull down the FILE menu, then NEW, then SYNTAX. Now you will have an open window in which to write the command syntax. Once you have written the syntax, you can run it directly by highlighting each line of syntax with the mouse and clicking on the RUN button (right arrow) at the top.

Here's the command syntax to recode COURTS:

```
RECODE COURTS(1=1)(2=3)(3=2).
```

Be sure to include a period at the end of each completed line of syntax. Also be sure to enter new value labels to reflect your recoding, since the labels do not change just because you've recoded the values themselves.

```
VALUE LABELS COURTS 1 'TOO HARSH' 2 'ABOUT RIGHT' 3
   'NOT HARSH ENOUGH'.
```

Also note that you have to indent the continuation line when a command is too long for one line (and don't break any words from one line to the next). Alternatively, you could use the command:

```
ADD VALUE LABELS COURTS 2 'ABOUT RIGHT' 3 'NOT
      HARSH ENOUGH'.
```

This is possible because you are just adding new labels for a portion of the values. [495–502]

4. How great is the problem of idiosyncratic variation in responses to questions? An illustration of the problem is available from the GSS94. Two questions were asked about whether extramarital sex is wrong. One question asked whether "Sex with a person other than one's spouse" is "always wrong," "almost always wrong," "sometimes wrong," or "not wrong at all." The other question asked whether "Extramarital sex [is] wrong." The response choices were "always wrong," "almost always wrong," "wrong only sometimes," or "not wrong at all." These are very minor differences in wording, but they make a difference.

Run the following commands in your syntax window.

```
FREQUENCIES XMARSEX, XMARSEX1.
CROSSTABS XMARSEX BY XMARSEX1.
```

The frequencies output shows you that the distribution of responses to the two questions was about the same. However, individuals were not entirely consistent in their responses. If you look down the diagonal in the crosstabulation, you see that most respondents (660) who said "always wrong" in response to one question gave the same response to the other. But a few did not (a total of 40), and so on through the table.

So some people who were asked nearly the same question two different times gave somewhat different responses. It may be that the slight differences in wording meant something to these responses—idiosyncratic variation or just some inconsistency due to chance. In any case, combining responses across several similar questions is likely to provide a more reliable measure. [82–85]

5. So now it's time to construct a multidimensional index. Fortunately, the GSS has a great many variables that are intended to be combined into indexes. I will walk you through some examples and give you some tips about index construction. Then you can practice constructing an index in your area of concern.

Inspect the distributions of the variables measuring confidence in institutions.

```
FREQUENCIES CONFINAN TO CONARMY.
```

You will note that the level of confidence varies markedly between different institutions. However, also note that all of these variables reflect the same type of question, all have the same response choices, and all the response choices are coded, numerically, in the same way (check this in the variable list).

Let us suppose that social theory and prior research highlight the importance and coherence of a general concept: confidence in institutions. This suggests that all these specific questions have this core concept in common. We then are justified in constructing an index to try to operationalize this concept.

You can construct the index, simply, as follows:

```
COMPUTE CONFIDI=MEAN.9(CONFINAN TO CONARMY).
VAR LABELS CONFIDI 'CONFIDENCE IN INSTITUTIONS'.
```

This computes a new variable, CONFIDI, that is the average response to these 13 questions. The *"TO"* can be used instead of naming all the variables because the variables are stored consecutively in the data file. The suffix to the *"MEAN"* argument, .9, stipulates that no case will receive a valid score on the index unless it has valid scores on at least 9 of the component variables.

If you like, at this point you can examine the distribution of cases on the CONFIDI index.

```
FREQUENCIES CONFIDI.
```

But was our assumption that these variables all reflected variation in the same concept an assumption that was supported by the data? We must check the "inter-item reliability" of the index.

```
RELIABILITY VARS=CONFINAN TO CONARMY/
   SCALE(CONFIDI)=CONFINAN TO CONARMY/SUMMARY=TOTAL.
```

Inspect the output from this command. At the bottom is the report "Alpha = .7688." Alpha, or "Cronbach's alpha," is a statistic used to assess the inter-item reliability of an index. It can range in value from 0 to 1, and when it has a value of at least .7, by convention the index is considered to be reliable. So this index meets the conventional criteria for reliability.

Look up at the "Item-Total Statistics," under the heading "Corrected Item-Total Correlation." The correlation coefficient ranges from 0 to ±1, with 0 indicating no linear association between the variables; +1 indicating that they are perfectly associated with each other, with values on one variable increasing in perfect linear fashion with values on the other; and −1 indicating a pattern of perfectly linear conjoint decrease. These correlations indicate that the strength of the association between each component variable (item) and the overall index is about the same—another indication of a reliable index. These items do share a common component.

But it is easy to make mistakes in index construction, particularly when you are using secondary data and you are not familiar with how each variable was measured. Let's look at an example.

Inspect the distributions of the variables measuring attitudes toward traditional gender roles among married couples.

```
FREQUENCIES FECHLD TO FEFAM.
```

It seems that these items are measuring the same general orientation and so could be combined in an index.

```
RELIABILITY VARS=FECHLD TO FEFAM/SCALE(SEXROLE)=
    FECHLD TO FEFAM/SUMMARY=TOTAL.
```

Now it seems there's a problem. Cronbach's alpha is only .0898. It seems that these items do not form a reliable index at all. But look up at the item-total correlations. You can see that the FECHLD variable has a moderate negative correlation with the index, −.5369, while the item-total correlation is positive for the other variables.

Look back at the frequencies for these variables. You will now note that increasing disagreement to the FECHLD statement (Mother working doesn't hurt children.) means more support for a traditional role for women, while increasing disagreement with the other statements means less support for a traditional female role.

This index-construction problem can be solved by recoding FECHLD.

```
RECODE FECHLD(4=1)(3=2)(2=3)(1=4).
```

Run this command and then again run the reliability procedure. Now we find that the alpha coefficient is .7848, reflecting a very reliable index after all. [99–100, 491–518]

6. Now try to construct an index yourself. As you should have learned by now, be very careful. Determine whether any recoding is needed first and then check your results. Make sure that any variables you combine in an index like this are quantitative. You can't use nominal variables (except for dichotomies) in this way. [82–85, 90–95]

7. We can also try to determine the validity of GSS measures using a construct validity approach. That is, we see if a variable of interest is related to those other variables that theory and prior research suggest it should be. If it is, our confidence in the measure's validity is increased.

I have just introduced you to the statistic known as the "correlation coefficient" or "Pearson's correlation coefficient," after statistician Karl Pearson. Let's use it in an assessment of the construct validity of the GSS measure of political orientation, POLVIEWS. Take a look at the POLVIEWS response choices in the variable list.

If POLVIEWS measures political beliefs along a liberal to conservative continuum, it should be associated with opposition to more welfare spending and to government efforts to reduce income differences. At least that is what political theory and research would lead us to expect. Is this the case?

```
CORR POLVIEWS WITH NATFARE, EQWLTH.
```

The correlations are both just a bit above .2—not strong, but in the expected direction. So we can take that as some preliminary evidence of the construct validity of the POLVIEWS measure. [98–99, 491–518]

8. Now propose a construct validity strategy for one of the measures you are working with. Use correlations to test your expectations. [98–99]

_____

_____

_____

_____

_____

_____

_____

_____

_____

_____

_____

_____

_____

_____

4 Causation

■ ■ ■ ■   **Text Objectives**

1. Define and distinguish *nomothetic* and *idiographic causal explanations*.

2. Identify which of the requirements for establishing causality are present in causal explanations.

3. Discuss the advantages and disadvantages of experimental and non-experimental approaches to meeting the criteria for causality, including attention to the relative merits of using statistical controls and randomization to meet the causal criterion of spuriousness.

4. Propose causal mechanisms and intervening variables for nomothetic causal explanations, and chart event histories in idiographic causal explanations.

5. Distinguish different types of longitudinal design: repeated cross-sectional designs, fixed-sample panel designs, and event-based designs.

6. Recognize ecological and reductionist fallacies in causal explanations that involve both individuals and groups.

Research in the News

1. A 1996 newspaper article (Barbara F. Meltz, "Are We Failing Our 4-year-olds?" *Boston Globe*, July 7, 1996: 64, 68) featured the research of psychologist David Weikart on children who had attended a special preschool program for 3- and 4-year-olds living in poverty. These children were subsequently much better off when they were re-interviewed as young adults. Their status was better in terms of earnings and overall finances, education levels, job histories, criminal records, drug problems, even avoiding teenage pregnancies.

"Can all this be attributed to *preschool?*" the reporter asked.

Here's a bit more information about the research design for you to consider before *you* answer that question. The children studied were African American children living in poverty. The study compared a sample of such children who were enrolled in a high-quality preschool with another sample of similar children who were not enrolled in such a school. The preschool children spent about 12 hours a week in the school for two years. The researchers studied these children until they were adults (the article I am citing was based on a report when the children were 27 years old).

What type of longitudinal design is this? Which criteria for causality are satisfied? Is there any basis for hesitating before concluding that the preschool experience was responsible for the better outcomes? Explain. How would you answer the reporter's question? [113–123]

_____

_____

_____

_____

_____

_____

_____

_____

_____

2. Should parents be punished for the crimes of their juvenile children? Fifteen states have laws, called "parental liability laws," that say they should. The laws reflect a common belief that juvenile delinquency is caused to a large extent by poor parenting.

Professor Richard Moran at Mt. Holyoke College, Sociology and Criminology Department, presented some evidence in an op-ed article that called this common belief about causality into question ("Why Blame His Parents When Johnny Breaks the Law?" *Boston Globe*, May 29, 1996: 13). First, he reviewed a study conducted in the mid-1960s by a federal agency. It found that states that had such laws had experienced a greater increase in juvenile delinquency over a six-year period than states that had not had such laws. In Toledo, Ohio, parental liability laws were vigorously enforced from 1937 to 1946, with more than 100 parents incarcerated as a result, but the delinquency rate did not decline. Moran also argues that such laws blame parents and so discourage juveniles from taking responsibility for their actions.

Do you think that parental neglect causes juvenile delinquency? Are you persuaded by the evidence Moran cited? Which criteria for establishing causality are met? What causal mechanism might "fit" with a parental responsibility perspective? What additional evidence would you like to have? [113–126]

_____

_____

_____

_____

_____

3. "Home life can nudge children to drugs, drink," asserted a newspaper article that summarized research on substance abuse among children (*Boston Globe*, May 13, 1996: 27–28). One of the research studies summarized, by psychologist Thomas Ashby Wills at Albert Einstein College of Medicine, followed 1,184 school children from the seventh to ninth grade. The 8% of kids who began to use alcohol, cigarettes, or marijuana heavily by the ninth grade tended to have many stresses in their lives, a low level of parental support, and academic problems. They also tended not to have parents or other caregivers who tried to listen to and understand their problems or school-based counseling and preventative programs.

One mother interviewed for the article explained her 12-year-old son's abuse of alcohol, LSD, and other drugs this way: "I think my son's problems started with the fact that we were poverty-stricken, and I was constantly worried about money, constantly short-tempered, and very irritable. There were four of them and one of me, and I couldn't give them the care and attention that children need. On top of that, my son was dyslexic and had problems in school. And we lived in the projects, where kids smoked pot in the hallways."

Is the mother's idiographic explanation of her son's substance abuse consistent with the nomothetic explanation from the research study? What additional variables does it suggest should be taken into account? What criteria for causality are established in the nomothetic research? What causal mechanisms would you suggest to link the effects of variables mentioned in the nomothetic explanation? How confident are you in the researcher's causal conclusions? [113–136]

_____

_____

_____

_____

_____

_____

_____

_____

_____

_____

_____

_____

_____

_____

_____

_____

_____

_____

4. Do banks discriminate on the basis of race when deciding whether to give mortgages to prospective home buyers? A comparison between mortgage applications in Boston found that 29% of applications from minority groups were rejected, compared to 11% of applications from whites (Peter Passell, "Race, Mortgages and Statistics: The Unending Debate Over a Study of Lending Bias." *The New York Times*, May 10, 1996: D1, D4).

Research by the Boston Federal Reserve Bank found that there was still a substantial difference in lending rates between these groups even after controlling statistically for 19 other variables, including applicants' income, net worth, marital status, and credit history. But then David Horne of the Federal Deposit Insurance Corporation found many cases for which there appeared to be faulty information. When he eliminated these cases and controlled statistically for two other variables (the banks' ability to verify applicants' credit information and their internal credit standards), no racial difference in rejection rates remained. Still other researchers continue to support the conclusion that there was lending bias.

Which causal criterion is the focus of attention in this debate? What technique was used to try to meet this criterion? Can you suggest a research design that would provide more definitive evidence? (*Hint:* some studies have relied on "testers" who are similar on all personal characteristics except race.) [113–126]

Short Essay Questions

1. A researcher interested in the causes of social unrest decides to try to obtain funding from two sources. One funding source sponsors traditional nomothetic research projects while the other favors idiographic causal investigation. Write a short paragraph that proposes a researchable nomothetic explanation of social unrest and another that proposes a researchable idiographic explanation. [109–112]

_____

_____

_____

_____

_____

_____

_____

_____

_____

_____

_____

_____

_____

_____

2. What is the counterfactual in nomothetic causal explanation and how well is it established in experimental and nonexperimental research? Is either the experimental or nonexperimental approach to establishing causality preferable for this reason? [111–112]

_____

_____

_____

_____

_____

_____

_____

_____

3. You read a letter to the editor in the school newspaper claiming that easy grading policies damage self-esteem. The letter writer points to a recent survey in which it was found that students tend to have lower levels of self-esteem in schools with easy grading policies than they do in schools with tougher grading policies. Construct an argument to challenge this causal reasoning. Review each of the criteria for causality and explain why they are or are not met in this instance. [113–126]

_____

_____

_____

_____

_____

_____

_____

_____

_____

_____

_____

4. A researcher hypothesizes that levels of stress vary with the poverty rate in communities. Briefly describe how you would collect data to evaluate this hypothesis: (a) using individuals as the units of analysis in a cross-sectional design; (b) using groups as the units of analysis in a cross-sectional design; and (c) using individuals as the units of analysis in a fixed-sample longitudinal design. [130–140]

_____

_____

5. Two studies are conducted of the relationship between gender and test performance. In study A, students are the units of analysis and it is found that men have higher test scores than women. Write a statement about this finding that would be reductionist. Explain why the statement is reductionist. In study B, classes are the units of analysis and it is found that classes in which the percentage of male students is higher also have, on average, higher test scores than is the case with classes having a lower percentage of male students. Write a statement about this finding that exemplifies an ecological fallacy. Explain what makes this statement an ecological fallacy. [138–140]

Multiple-Choice Questions

1. A researcher seeks to determine whether individuals report more satisfaction with their lives if they are promoted on their jobs. It can be said that the researcher is seeking to develop _____. [109–112]

    a. an idiographic causal explanation
    b. a nomothetic causal explanation
    c. a reliable measure
    d. a journalistic account
    e. a historicist explanation

2. Dickson was born in 1926 and grew up during the Great Depression. His parents were preoccupied with keeping bread on the table and did not spend time with Dickson. As a result, he grew up plagued by feelings of self-doubt. He showed some promise as a writer, but began to drink heavily after a failed relationship and was unable to continue to write. He began to drink even more frequently. As an explanation for Dickson's alcoholism, this could be termed _____. [109–115]

    a. nomothetic
    b. experimental
    c. ideological
    d. normative
    e. idiographic

3. An employee survey is conducted in a study of the effects of stress. The researcher measures the level of stress felt by each employee at work as well as the traffic congestion that each employee experiences while driving to work. After analyzing the data obtained, the researcher concludes that traffic congestion caused an increase in stress among employees. This illustrates _____ approach to establishing causal relations. [109–115]

    a. an idiographic
    b. an experimental
    c. a nonexperimental
    d. an unsystematic
    e. an idiosyncratic

4. Dr. Magneto finds that people who are college graduates are more likely to attend the symphony than people who have less education. She concludes that symphony attendance is caused by education. This conclusion _____. [113–129]

    a. is valid on its face as a nomothetic causal conclusion
    b. violates the requirement that a cause be associated with its effect
    c. is valid for urban residence, but not for poverty
    d. violates the principle that correlation does not prove causation
    e. exemplifies the weakness of idiographic causal explanation

5. An experimental study has found that depressed persons who attend therapy sessions are more successful in lessening their depressed feelings than depressed persons who do not attend therapy sessions. In the conclusions to a report on this experiment, the researchers suggest that it will be important for future studies to determine whether the therapy effect was due to the personality of the therapist, the technique the therapist used, or the time for reflection provided to the client by the sessions. This suggestion reflects a concern with _____. [113–124]

    a. causal mechanisms
    b. spurious relationships
    c. faulty randomization
    d. time order
    e. frequency of association

6. Dr. George Tamino conducts an experiment to test the effect of reprimands on task performance. He randomly assigns 30 student volunteers to two different rooms where both groups are asked to perform a simple, repetitive task for one hour. First he measures their task performance for a fixed duration of time. Then he reprimands the students in one group for poor performance, while allowing the other group to continue to work, uninterrupted, in another room. At the end of the hour he measures their task performance again. He finds that members of the group that was reprimanded decreased their task performance more than members of the group that was not reprimanded. He concludes that reprimands lead to poorer task performance. His causal conclusion _____. [113–124]

    a. is valid because of randomization
    b. cannot be valid unless he uses statistical controls
    c. is valid because time order is clear
    d. is invalid until it is replicated outside of the laboratory
    e. may not be valid because of differences due to chance

7. A researcher conducts a cross-sectional survey and finds that employed students receive better grades than do unemployed students. Before it can be concluded that the relationship between employment and grades can

be considered a causal one, which of the following criteria must be met? [117–124]

    a. time order
    b. nonspuriousness
    c. causal mechanism
    d. time order and nonspuriousness
    e. time order and causal mechanism

8. A researcher studies the impact of having lived in a community that experienced a large riot. Data are collected from a sample of young adults in the community shortly after the riot. Ten years later, a new sample of young adults is again drawn from the same community. This would be termed _____. [130–138]

    a. a cross-sectional design
    b. a repeated cross-sectional design
    c. an event-based design
    d. a fixed-sample panel design
    e. a group-level design

9. The average level of career commitment is higher in corporations that have higher average salaries. The conclusion is suggested that employees who are paid more tend to be more committed to their careers. This conclusion _____. [138–140]

    a. may be in error due to an ecological fallacy
    b. may be in error due to reductionism
    c. is necessarily in error due to an ecological fallacy
    d. is necessarily in error due to reductionism
    e. does not involve a potential problem stemming from the units of analysis

10. Compare the following two causal models: (A) Greater performance pressure results in higher levels of anxiety, which in turn decrease quality of performance. When anxiety level is statistically controlled, the relation between performance pressure and quality of performance disappears. (B) Low levels of performance pressure result in less anxiety and in better quality of performance. When performance pressure is statistically controlled, the relation between anxiety and quality of performance disappears. What is the causal role of social support in models A and B? [119–121]

    a. intervening in A, extraneous in B
    b. intervening in both
    c. extraneous in both
    d. extraneous in A, intervening in B
    e. no causal role in either A or B

Mini-Projects

Why Did They Do That?

You are to construct an idiographic explanation of someone's decision to enroll in a particular college, start a particular job, move, or join some social or political group.

1. Identify a friend, fellow student, or other acquaintance whom you can interview for about 30 minutes. Tell this person that you will be asking questions about his or her decision to. . . .

2. Find an agreeable time and place for the interview. Explain to the respondent that you are going to ask questions about his or her decision and things that preceded that decision. Mention that it is for a class project.

3. You can begin asking the respondent to tell you about his or her decision. As he or she does so, start to ask questions about why antecedent and subsequent steps occurred, such as "How did that happen?" Jot down notes to help you remember each explanation.

4. Stop the interview when you have filled in the major steps in the sequence of events leading up to the respondent's decision. Review and elaborate on your notes.

5. Chart the causal sequence leading to the decision with a diagram like that used by Griffin in his event-structure analysis of a lynching (Exhibit 4.9, text p. 128). Summarize the proposed causal explanation in a few paragraphs.

6. How confident are you with your explanation of the respondent's decision? What alternative explanations could link these and other events to the decision?

Discovery!

You will develop a historicist explanation for a war or social movement.

1. Locate a book presenting the history of a war or social movement. Be sure that it includes the period that preceded the event. Read (or scan) the book.

2. Jot down the steps in the causal sequence leading up to the event.

3. Summarize the causal sequence in a diagram like that used by Griffin (Exhibit 4.9, text p. 128).

4. Write an idiographic explanation of the event.

5. How confident are you in your explanation? Can you think of any alternative explanations that are consistent with the author's presentation?

6. Develop a possible nomothetic explanation for such wars or social movements based on the factors identified as important in the idiographic explanation. Which variables would have to be measured in order to test this explanation?

Social Contagion?

This experiment must be conducted with one or two other participants. It is an effort to test the effect that one person's interest in a product has on the actions of others.

1. Pick a store display window that faces a busy sidewalk or mall interior. To prepare for the experiment, observe pedestrians going past the window, noting the number passing and their behaviors.

2. The experimental treatment is to be one of the participants looking appreciatively at something in the display window. Develop a plan to observe the behaviors of others outside the window. This is to involve one or two of the participants standing unobtrusively so they can observe people outside of the window and count the number of times that these people glance in the window. See if you can develop some rules for classifying a behavior as a "glance in the window."

3. Begin the experiment by counting the number of people who pass the window and the number of times they glance in the window over a five-minute period. Be sure that you and the other participants involved in observing are far enough away that you won't be noticed by the passersby. Also be sure to begin the observational period when no one is standing and gazing in the window. Record the counts in a small notebook without attracting attention yourself. Now have one participant stand in front of the window and gaze intently into it for five minutes. Repeat the count.

4. Now repeat the cycle of observing with and without the observer present. Continue until you have completed five cycles of the process.

5. Calculate the number of glances per passerby for each five-minute observational period. If counts are available from two or more observers, average them before performing the calculations.

6. Calculate an overall average "glances per passerby" for the periods when your window gazer was present and when he or she was not.

7. Was there a difference in the glances made by passersby based on whether someone was already observing? Comment on the size of the difference and the possibility of influences other than the presence of your window gazer.

Design Weaknesses

This project requires reviewing a number of journal articles.

1. Locate a journal that includes many experimental or longitudinal studies. Evaluation journals and journals in psychology, social psychology, and psychiatry are good choices.

2. Identify all articles reporting experimental and longitudinal studies in at least five journal issues.

3. For each selected article, determine which criteria for causality were established. Note whether a causal mechanism was discussed. Record the percentage of initial cases lost to attrition. Identify the units of analysis.

4. Review the conclusions and note whether each of the features you noted in question 3 was discussed. Give each article a "grade" based on the extent to which conclusions were not qualified, or were in error, due to the absence of one or more causal criteria, failure to identify a causal mechanism, sample attrition, or the occurrence of an ecological or reductionist fallacy.

5. Summarize what you have learned about flaws in research design and research conclusions in this type of research.

Exploring the General Social Survey

1. The causal criteria of association, time order, nonspuriousness, and identifying a causal mechanism can each be examined with the GSS data, although we are limited by the cross-sectional survey design in our ability to establish time order. For a demonstration, we will test the hypothesis that drinkers are more likely to watch X-rated movies than are nondrinkers.

2. Generate a crosstabulation to describe the association between drinking and watching X-rated movies.

```
CROSSTABS XMOVIE BY DRINK/CELLS=COL.
```

Compare the percentages in the columns for those who said "yes" they drink or "no" they don't drink. What percentage of the drinkers said they had seen an X-rated movie in the last year? What about the nondrinkers? So our hypothesis is supported. [515–518]

_____

_____

_____

_____

_____

3. But we know that we have now only demonstrated an association between the two variables. What about the criterion of time order? With cross-sectional data, we can't establish time order unless the value of the independent variable (drinking, in our hypothesis) was established before the value of the dependent variable (XMOVIE). Perhaps you could make a case for this, but it wouldn't be on very firm ground. We'll just have to accept some doubt on this score.

You learned in the text that nonexperimental designs try to establish the criterion of nonspuriousness through statistical controls. Let's check for one possibly extraneous influence on our two variables: gender. The possibility is that gender influences both the propensity to drink and to watch X-rated movies, creating a spurious relationship between them. (Compare to Exhibit 4.5, text p. 120.)

```
CROSSTABS XMOVIE, DRINK BY SEX/CELLS=COL.
```

These tables demonstrate that both XMOVIE and DRINK are associated with gender, as we would expect if gender created a spurious relationship between them. But we need to take one more step.

```
CROSSTABS XMOVIE BY DRINK BY SEX/CELLS=COL.
```

Now compare the percent of male drinkers who had seen an X-rated movie in the last year to the percent of male nondrinkers who had. Whereas before we took account of gender, the difference here was about 20% (25% v. 13%); for males only, the difference between drinkers and nondrinkers is now down to about 10% (32% v. 21%). And the same change is apparent in the table for women.

So we can say that the relationship between drinking and watching X-rated movies is at least partially spurious due to the effect of gender. [119–121, 515–518]

4. Test a hypothesis related to your GSS research question using cross-tabulation. Now identify a variable that could plausibly play an extraneous role in this relationship. Test for this possibility with another crosstabulation. *Be sure that you recode any variables with many values to no more than three or four categories before you generate any crosstabulation with those variables.* [501–502]

5. We'll evaluate the possibility of an intervening variable in a proposed causal chain with the correlation statistic that we used in chapter 3. Our independent variable will be education, the dependent variable will be respondent's income, and the proposed intervening variable will be respondent's occupational prestige (as of 1980). The idea is that education influences the prestige of the occupation people obtain, and then income is influenced by the occupation.

If this proposed causal chain is correct, then all three variables should be related to each other.

```
CORR EDUC, RINCOM91, PRESTG80.
```

Examine the "correlation matrix." There are three different correlations in it, reflecting the three pairs of variables. The correlation between income and both prestige and education is above .3. The correlation between education and occupational prestige is above .5. So all three variables are associated. [115–117]

6. Now determine whether the association between education and income disappears when we "break the causal chain" by statistically controlling for occupational prestige, the intervening variable.

```
PARTIAL CORR EDUC WITH RINCOM91 BY PRESTG80.
```

The correlation between income and education has been reduced to .146, after prestige was controlled. So the relationship has not disappeared, but it has been substantially reduced. Our hypothesis that occupational prestige intervenes in the relationship between education and income is partially supported. [119–124]

7. You can use the same approach to test for a possible intervening variable in one of your hypotheses. Be sure that any variables you use in a correlational analysis are quantitative, and that none of the values are "out of order." [119–124]

5 Sampling

■ ■ ■ ■ **Text Objectives**

1. Define *generalizability* and its relationship to the terms *census, nonprobability sampling method, representativeness, bias, sampling error, true value of a statistic,* and *statistical inference.*

2. Evaluate the quality of different obtained samples.

3. Distinguish *elements, sample, sampling frame, population,* and *target population* and explain how they are related in the process of drawing probability samples.

4. Describe nonprobability sampling methods and know when they are appropriate and what their advantages and disadvantages are in comparison with probability sampling methods.

5. Draw a simple random sample, systematic random samples with and without replacement, a quota sample, and disproportionate and proportionate stratified samples.

6. Explain the concept of a sampling distribution, its relation to sampling error, its role in calculating the standard error, confidence limits and confidence intervals, and its variation in response to simple random sampling, stratified sampling, and cluster sampling.

Research in the News

1. New York and other big cities sued the federal government in 1988 in an attempt to avoid an undercount in the 1990 census of members of racial minority groups and of individuals who live in big cities (Linda Greenhouse. "High Court Rules Results Are Valid in Census of 1990." *The New York Times,* March 21, 1996: A1, A22). However, the suit failed (the Supreme Court finally rejected it in March 1996). Although the census missed only 2% of the total population, this included 4.8% of the African American population and 5.2% of the Hispanic population.

What the plaintiffs had sought was the use of sampling methods to adjust the 1990 census figures. The idea was that by sampling in areas where undercounts appeared to be likely, and then devoting substantial resources to securing a very high rate of response from all persons in the sample, an accurate estimate of the true fraction of individuals who were undercounted, and of their characteristics, would result. The new information would be used to weight the census figures to adjust for the undercounted population.

Although a special survey with a sample of 400,000 people demonstrated that the adjustment could be done, the Supreme Court concluded that the Commerce Department was within its constitutional rights in the way it had conducted the census. No adjustment was made.

How does this controversy reflect the logic of sampling? Do you believe that this is an instance when sampling can be used to supplement the effort to conduct a complete census? Would you support a proposal for changing the entire census to a sample survey? Explain your reasoning. [148–152]

_____

_____

_____

_____

2. Now comes the census plan for the year 2000. The Census Bureau announced in February 1996 plans to actually count 90 percent of the population and rely on sampling to determine the number and characteristics of the rest (Steven A. Holmes, "In a First, 2000 Census Is to Use Sampling." *The New York Times*, February 29, 1996: A18). Census Bureau Director Martha Farnsworth Riche explained, "What we intend to do to meet our twin goals of reducing costs and increasing accuracy is to make a much greater use of widely accepted scientific statistical methods, and sampling is first and foremost among them."

The reason that a sample makes so much sense to the Census Bureau is that so much money has to be spent in getting a substantial number of people to participate. Back in 1970, 85% of the population mailed their census form in. In 1990, only 63% of Americans returned their mail-in census form; the rest were the object of expensive follow-up efforts by interviewers. By focusing on a sample of the initial respondents, more intensive follow-up efforts can be used without increasing costs.

But the new sampling plan was opposed by many members of Congress. What arguments do you think can be made, pro and con? Which arguments do you find to be more persuasive? If you support the sampling plan, are there *any* situations in which you feel a census would be preferable to a sample? If you favor continuation of a complete census, are there *any* situations in which you think a sample would be preferable to a census? Explain your reasoning. [148–152]

_____

_____

_____

_____

_____

_____

_____

_____

_____

_____

_____

_____

_____

3. Findings from a survey of sexual practices in America by social scientists Gagnon, Laumann, Michael, and Michaels surprised many people (Tamar Lewin, "Sex in America: Faithfulness in Marriage Is Overwhelming." _The New York Times_, October 7, 1994: A1, A18). While previous sex studies had suggested that marital infidelity and a wide range of sex practices were rather common, the new study indicated that most Americans were involved in committed relationships and had sex only in rather ordinary ways.

The discrepancy had a lot to do with sampling. Previous studies had relied on samples of volunteers—patients in a sex clinic or individuals who filled out a questionnaire in a magazine. The social scientists' sex survey instead relied on a national sample that was selected using standard random sampling methods. About four out of every five of those contacted for a face-to-face interview agreed to participate. (Rates of return for magazine surveys are often only a few percent.)

What do you think might motivate individuals to volunteer for a survey about sexual practices? What might lead to different response rates to a survey in a magazine and a request by an in-person interviewer? What do you think might distinguish the 20% of persons contacted who declined to participate in the social scientists' sex survey?

In what other areas of research would you expect researchers to have major difficulties in securing an adequate rate of response? Aside from ignorance about research methods, what might influence people to accept "as gospel" findings from surveys about deviant behaviors that had very biased samples? [152–158]

_____

_____

_____

_____

_____

_____
_____
_____
_____
_____
_____
_____
_____

4. Careful studies of long-term results of medical treatments have become possible for many illnesses in recent years because of the development by managed care organizations of computerized databases on millions of patients (Holcomb B. Noble, "Linking Technology and Health Groups to Find Best Cure." *The New York Times*, September 24, 1995: 32).

Consider pooling databases to generate a massive database on all Americans enrolled in HMOs. Describe a cluster sampling plan for selecting cases from the databases for such a study. Describe a stratified sampling plan. [170–174]

_____
_____
_____
_____
_____
_____
_____
_____
_____
_____
_____
_____

Short Essay Questions

1. A university counseling office includes a survey in a packet of materials mailed to new students. The survey is designed to measure potential interest in counseling services. Twenty percent of the new students complete and return the survey. Comparing this sample of new students to university records for all new students indicates that the students who responded are similar to all new students in terms of average age, high school GPA, percent female, and percent in each major racial and ethnic category. Based on this information, how successful would you say the sampling strategy was? Explain your reasoning, referring to the concepts of representativeness and bias and the nature of random selection. [152–161]

2. You are to design a stratified sampling strategy for a survey of the relationship between education and economic achievement. Describe a sampling design in which the population is all adults and the sampling elements are individuals. Define in your description the sampling frame and the sampling units. What are the advantages and disadvantages of this design compared to a simple random sample? [168–172]

_____

_____

_____

_____

_____

_____

_____

_____

3. What motivates the use of nonprobability sampling methods? Review the four nonprobability sampling methods, identify reasons for their use, and indicate circumstances when each might be appropriate. [161–165]

_____

_____

_____

_____

_____

_____

_____

_____

_____

_____

_____

_____

_____

_____

4. Describe the unique features of simple random samples, stratified samples, and cluster samples. Discuss the advantages and disadvantages of each. Include in your discussion consideration of sampling error and its sources. [165–180]

_____
_____
_____
_____
_____
_____
_____
_____
_____
_____
_____
_____
_____
_____
_____
_____
_____

5. Explain how a statistical inference can be made from a sample to a population. Discuss in your explanation the concept of a normal distribution and the foundation it provides for estimating population parameters. [177–180]

_____
_____
_____
_____
_____
_____
_____
_____
_____
_____
_____
_____
_____
_____

Multiple-Choice Questions

1. A college uses a placement test to predict the academic performance of its students. A testing service has found that the test does indeed predict academic performance, but it has only studied applicants to a community college. A woman who was denied admission to a four-year college sues the school. She claims in her suit that the test cannot be used to predict her academic performance, since it has been used only at a community college. This claim raises a question of _____. [149]

    a. cross-population generalizability
    b. sample representativeness
    c. nonprobability sampling
    d. measurement reliability
    e. conceptual definition

2. Inmates in a large prison are selected from the prison's roster for a study of fear of crime in the prison. The researchers discuss in their results the implications of their findings for "fear of crime in contemporary prisons." In sampling terminology, prisoners are the _____, the prison roster is the _____, and prisoners in contemporary prisons are the _____. [153]

    a. elements, sampling frame, target population
    b. elements, sampling frame, population
    c. elements, sample, target population
    d. elements, sample, population
    e. sampling units, sample, target population

3. A researcher must design a sampling strategy that will yield the highest quality sample possible of a population having 5,000 members. His strategy is constrained by limited financial resources and insufficient time, so that he has only the following possible options. Which option should he choose? [158–162, 168–169, 180–182]

    a. sampling method = availability, sample size = 200, rate of nonresponse = 5%
    b. sampling method = random, sample size = 200, rate of nonresponse = 5%
    c. sampling method = random, sample size = 400, rate of nonresponse = 20%
    d. sampling method = random, sample size = 400, rate of nonresponse = 20%
    e. sampling method = availability, sample size = 500, rate of nonresponse = 5%

4. What is the probability of selection in each of the following situations? A 3 after spinning a pentagon with sides numbered consecutively from 1 to 5? Someone from Illinois in a random draw of one student from a school in which there are 500 Illinoisans out of a total student body of 3,000? [165]

    a. .5, .167
    b. .2, .3
    c. .2, .01
    d. .1, .167
    e. .2, .167

5. The blue-collar labor force has shrunk in Saskatoon, and there are now only 10 firms with substantial numbers of blue-collar employees. The Saskatoon city council requests proposals from research organizations for a survey to describe the city's blue-collar labor force. One of the proposals submitted includes the following sampling design: First, a small local corporation with many blue-collar employees has agreed to be surveyed. The researchers will go to the corporation on randomly selected days for two months and select employees for interviews. The selection process will occur on the shop floor, but the interviews will be conducted after work. Of the 92 tables in the cafeteria, the researchers will ask for employee volunteers at every fifth table. This sampling design can be referred to as _____ sample. [161–174]

    a. an availability
    b. a quota
    c. a simple random
    d. a multistage cluster
    e. a stratified random

6. A study is conducted of suburban séance clubs. Using a contact at one séance club, the researcher is able to interview each club's leader. The interview covers methods of séancing and sources of insight in séances. The sampling method would be termed _____. [161–174]

    a. availability
    b. quota
    c. purposive
    d. multistage cluster
    e. snowball

7. Voters are sampled randomly from three Canadian provinces. The same case-selection procedures are used for each province. Features of the provinces and the samples are:

	Characteristics of Province A	Three Samples Province B	Province C
Pop. Size	100,000	10,000,000	900,000
Sample Size	250	500	500
Income Range	$10–75,000/yr.	$10–75,000/yr.	$50–75,000/yr.

In which sample(s) can we place the most confidence for an estimate of average income? [178]

    a. Province A
    b. Province B
    c. Province C
    d. Province A or B
    e. Province B or C

8. You must draw a sample of 5,000 from the population of a large city in order to estimate public park usage. A list of all city residents and their incomes is available from city hall. Which sampling procedure will minimize sampling error? [162, 168–174]

    a. a multistage cluster sample, using counties as clusters
    b. a simple random sample, using a computer program to generate random numbers
    c. a proportionate stratified sample, using income for strata
    d. a systematic random sample, using the Census bureau listing
    e. a quota sample, with quotas set on the basis of income

9. A population has 2,000 college graduates, 3,000 high school grads, and 500 elementary school grads. A sample that is a disproportionate stratified random sample of that population on the basis of education has 100 college grads, 200 high school grads, and 100 elementary school grads. The weight that must be applied to the 3,000 high school grads so that their sample numbers match the educational distribution of the population is _____. [171–172]

    a. 20.1
    b. 1.09
    c. .68
    d. 2.68
    e. .5

10. Which of the following might be a good variable on which to stratify a population prior to sampling? [170–172]

    a. Social Security number
    b. school attended
    c. county
    d. educational level
    e. church

11. Which of the following pairs does not match a sampling strategy with an appropriate variable on which to base that strategy? [170–174]

    a. cluster/income
    b. stratified/education
    c. cluster/town
    d. cluster/church
    e. stratified/gender

12. A researcher obtains a list of all voluntary organizations in a state. She draws a random sample of 125 of the voluntary organizations on this list. She then obtains a list of members from the organization presidents at each of the 125 organizations and interviews a random sample of 5 teachers at each school. This is a _____ sample. [164, 168–174]

    a. purposive
    b. simple random
    c. systematic random
    d. stratified
    e. cluster

13. A statistician estimates the mean annual expenditures on illegal drugs in the population, using data obtained with a random sample of 100 cases. He determines that he can be 95% confident that the true mean in the population is between $27 and $105. Which of the following statements would *not* be true? The confidence interval would _____. [177–178]

    a. be larger if the sample had 100 cases
    b. be smaller if the degree of confidence were higher
    c. vary from sample to sample
    d. be larger if it used the 99% confidence limits
    e. be smaller if the population were more homogeneous

Mini-Projects

Making a Snowball

Select a topic for investigation that focuses on a student characteristic or behavior that is relatively uncommon, unorganized, and not readily apparent. Some possibilities are strict vegetarians, guitar players, recreational long-distance runners, and wilderness campers. (Yes, that's right—I'm avoiding sensitive topics.)

1. Compose two questions to ask persons in this population. For example: Can you tell me how you got into this activity? What do you like and dislike about it?

2. Identify a student in this population, using personal knowledge, a newspaper article, or a friend's reference.

3. Ask this person if you can ask them a few questions about the activity for a class project. If they agree, ask them the two questions and then ask them who else they could suggest as participants in this activity. If they decline, just ask them if they can recommend anyone else you could talk to about the activity.

4. Repeat this process, asking the new contacts for names of people whom they would recommend.

5. You can stop after you have three sets of names: from the initial contact, from the persons he or she recommended, and then from the additional contacts these persons recommended.

6. Write up a description and critique of this snowball sampling process. How many persons were in your final list? What biases, if any, seemed to be apparent in the recommendations of people who were recommended by other people who were recommended by other people, and so on? How many stages do you think there would have to be to your snowballing to develop a complete list of all students involved in this activity on your campus? In what circumstances do you think a snowball sampling strategy would be most useful? What would be the major sources of bias?

A Simple Random Sample

Focus for this project on the employment, housing, or car ads in a daily newspaper, being sure to use the issue for a day of the week when there are many such ads. If you use the newspaper for a large city, you might team up with another classmate to reduce the work each of you has to do. Plan to draw a random sample of 25 ads.

1. Identify the pages on which the employment, car, house, or rental ads appear.

2. Number consecutively all the ads of the type you select. Note the total number of such ads.

3. Turn to the table of random numbers (appendix, text p. 519). Determine the number of digits that you will need in your numbers to identify cases in your "population" of ads. (For example, if there are 152 ads, you will need to use 3-digit numbers.) Decide on a rule for selecting numbers in the table, such as every number as you move from right to left across a row and then from left to right back across the next row. Close your eyes and pick a starting point. Following your selection rule, write down the first 15 numbers that you encounter that fall within the range of ad numbers (if there are 152 ads, this means that you should write down the first 15 numbers between 1 and 152).

4. Circle the ads corresponding to the numbers you have written down from the random number table.

5. Record one or two characteristics of each ad. These might be the type of job advertised, the community where a house or apartment is located, whether the asking price is listed, and the asking price for the house.

6. If you used types of jobs or communities as a characteristic, review these types and, if it seems warranted, group them together in a more limited number of categories (for example, white-collar and blue-collar, or north side and south side).

7. Now tally up the characteristics (for example, how many housing ads listed an asking price and how many didn't). Calculate an arithmetic average for the prices or salaries you recorded (add up all the prices, or salaries, and then divide by the total number of prices or salaries listed). These are your "sample statistics."

8. Repeat step 7 for the entire set of ads. The resulting figures are your "population parameters."

9. Compare the sample statistics and population parameters. How well did your small random sample represent the true values for these characteristics in the population from which you sampled? Did you have any trouble defining the sampling frame (the list of ads in your population)?

A Stratified Random Sample

Repeat the steps in the previous mini-project, but this time select a population for study that can easily be arranged by "strata." Possibilities are college courses (arranged by department), TV shows (arranged by day of the week), stock prices (arranged by industry), used car ads (arranged by year), housing prices (arranged by neighborhood), and so on. Alter the steps as indicated below.

1. Count the number of cases in each stratum.

2. Decide on the number of cases you will select from each stratum to collect a proportionate or a disproportionate stratified sample. (For example, you may select the same number of cases in each stratum; if the strata differ in total number of cases, this will result in a disproportionate stratified sample.)

3. Number the cases consecutively within strata, starting at 1 each time.

4. Select the required numbers from each stratum, going back to the random number table (appendix 4, text p. 519) to generate a new list of eligible numbers for each stratum.

5. Calculate the sample statistics based on combining the results across strata.

A Systematic Random Sample

Arrange with a professor teaching a large lecture class to carry out this study.

1. Review the class roster. Identify the total number of students registered and the number of men and women in the class. You are to draw a sample of about 20 students. Decide on a sampling fraction for your sampling project so that you will obtain 20 students in your sample. (For example, if there are 100 students in the class, your sampling fraction will be 1/5.)

2. Arrive outside the lecture hall at least 15 minutes before the class begins. Station yourself before the entrance door. (If there is more than one entrance, you should pick the one that is most used or collaborate with other students who will watch the other entrances.)

3. Pick a number, using a random process, between 1 and your sampling fraction number (between 1 and 6, if the sampling fraction is 1/6). You might roll a die, flip a few coins, or use the random number table. (If you use coins, you can designate certain equally frequent combinations of heads and tails to represent different starting numbers. For example, to generate a starting number between 1 and 4, you can flip two coins: 1 = 1 tail and then 1 head, 2 = 1 head and then 1 tail, 3 = 2 tails, 4 = 2 heads.)

4. Prepare a note card with two columns under the headings *Female* and *Male*. Observe carefully as students enter the door. Make a check under the

appropriate gender heading for the student who enters the door in the position corresponding to your starting number. Now make a check corresponding to the gender of each subsequent student who enters the class in the position corresponding to your sampling fraction (for example, if the sampling fraction is 1/6, this might be the 2nd student, then the 8th student, the 14th student, the 20th student, and so on).

5. Add up the number of women and men in your two columns. Then calculate the percent female. This is your sample statistic.

6. Compare the sample statistic to the percent female for the class as a whole (the population parameter).

7. How well did the sample represent the distribution of gender in the population from which you sampled? What problems did you encounter in your sampling? Were you able to adhere to the procedures? Is there likely to be any systematic bias in your sample?

Cluster Sampling

You will experiment with cluster sampling techniques.

1. Obtain a map of a city or town that shows individual blocks. Number all the blocks (if this is a large city, you might focus on only one neighborhood).

2. Record 10 random numbers from the random number table in appendix 4 (text p. 519), omitting all numbers greater than the number of blocks in the city, town, or neighborhood.

3. Select the 10 blocks from the map that correspond to your 10 random numbers.

4. Now visit each block; or if that's not safe or feasible, check with the town hall or the local library to find out if you can obtain a map that includes each building. Count the number of buildings on each block and note the approximate number of dwelling units in each building.

5. Again based on the table of random numbers, draw a random sample of buildings on each of the blocks in your sample.

6. Review the cluster sampling process. Are there any sources of systematic bias? [*Hint:* How similar were the number of buildings on the sampled blocks? How many multifamily buildings were there?] What could you add to the sampling strategy to avoid such biases?

Exploring the General Social Survey

1. Request the frequencies (FRE) of a quantitative variable having at least five values. Include in the request HIST=NORMAL, and STAT=MEAN, MEDIAN,STDDEV.

```
FRE PRESTG80/HIST=NORMAL/PERCENTILES=2.5 33.3 66.7
    97.5/STATS=MEAN,SEMEAN,STDDEV,VARIANCE,MEDIAN.
```

How well does the distribution approximate a normal distribution? How closely do the cut-points requested correspond to one and two standard deviation units above and below the mean? [177–181]

_____

_____

_____

_____

_____

_____

_____

_____

2. You will learn about random sampling by treating the GSS94 sample as if it were a population from which you can sample. Generate the mean occupational PRESTG80 for 10 random samples from the GSS94 sample. You will then plot the resulting sampling distribution.

```
TEMPORARY.
SET SEED=8-digit number.
SAMPLE 10 FROM 2000.
DESCRIPTIVES PRESTG80.
```

Repeat 10 times, changing the 8-digit number each time. Write down the mean for each sample.

_____

_____

_____

_____

_____

_____

_____

_____

3. Now repeat the previous steps, but increase the sample size to 25.

SAMPLE 25 FROM 2000.

Write down your results.

_____

_____

_____

_____

_____

_____

_____

4. Now plot the sample means on graph paper, separately for steps 2 and 3. The horizontal axis should be used to plot the sample mean, while the vertical axis should indicate the number of samples corresponding to a particular mean. [180–181]

_____

_____

_____

_____

_____

_____

_____

_____

5. Look at both sampling distributions. How well does each begin to approximate a normal curve? Where is the mean of the sampling distributions (compared to the mean for the entire GSS sample)? How do the two sampling distributions differ? Does it appear that the sampling distribution based on means of larger samples ($N = 25$) is more compact than the sampling distribution of smaller samples ($N = 10$)? [179–182]

6. Calculate the 95% and 99% confidence intervals for the mean PRESTG80 in the total sample (see first output requested, step 1 above). Check yourself by using SPSS to calculate the confidence intervals, as follows:

```
EXAMINE VAR=PRESTG80/PLOT=NONE/CINTERVAL 95.
EXAMINE VAR=PRESTG80/PLOT=NONE/CINTERVAL 99.
```

State your confidence in the obtained interval estimates. [178–180]

6 Validity in Three Dimensions: Integration and Review

■ ■ ■ ■ **Text Objectives**

1. Evaluate in particular research designs the trade-offs between features that attempt to maximize measurement validity, causal validity, and generalizability.

2. Identify research findings in which there is a likelihood of contextual effects.

3. Write a thorough critique of an empirical research article, including methods used to achieve measurement validity, causal validity, and generalizability.

4. Describe the limitations imposed by the use of archival data.

5. Appreciate the central role of the research problem (or question) in research design.

Research in the News

1. The "cold facts" reveal why sending more convicted criminals to prison will not have much effect on the crime rate, according to a magazine article (David C. Anderson, "The Crime Funnel." *The New York Times Magazine*, June 12, 1994: 56–58). Although 25 million serious crimes are committed in the U.S. each year, only 15 million are reported to police and only 1.9 million result in convictions. So imprisoning more than the current 500,000 convicts per year is not likely to have much impact on the 25 million total.

A survey by the National Institute of Justice revealed part of the mechanism behind the crime funnel. Many crime victims didn't think the crimes were serious enough or the odds of arresting the criminals or recovering stolen property were high enough to bother reporting the crimes.

Suggest alternative measures that might help to reveal more about why people don't report crimes. Consider measures involving observation, questions, and using available data. [196–210]

2. After several incidents of crimes or tragedies occurring in which some people appeared to imitate TV violence in real life, media attention focused on the possibility of a causal connection between violence on TV and in real life (William Grimes, "Does Life Imitate Violence on Film?" *The New York Times*, November 30, 1995: B1, B3). Some research indicates that media violence leads to violence in real life across different cultures. But media defenders have suggested that the movies are easy targets and that the real causes of violence are being overlooked.

Propose experimental and nonexperimental research designs for studying the impact of TV violence on the propensity of viewers to commit violent acts. What measures would you use, which possible extraneous variables would you try to take into account, what concerns for generalizability would you have, and how would you identify causal mechanisms? [211–214]

Short Essay Questions

1. Research design lesson 15 is that "Most research questions cannot adequately be answered with just one study using a single research design." Explain why this is so. Refer in your answer to some of the other research design lessons and to research studies described in the text. [214]

_____

_____

_____

_____

_____

_____

_____

_____

_____

_____

_____

_____

_____

_____

2. What ethical issues might emerge in research concerning the impact of a family counseling program on teenagers' propensity for delinquency? What would be the ethical problems posed by different possible measures, designs to establish causality, and sampling strategies? Describe and justify the ethics of the research elements that you would prefer. [207–210]

_____

_____

_____

_____

_____
_____
_____
_____
_____
_____
_____
_____
_____
_____
_____
_____
_____
_____
_____
_____

3. Outline a plan for conducting research to test hypotheses about the impact of unemployment on families. The research plan can involve either individuals or groups (any aggregate) as the units of analysis and collection of either cross-sectional or longitudinal data. Describe the type of measures you would use, the approach you would take to establishing causality, and your sampling strategy. Write an argument that justifies your selections. [210–214]

_____
_____
_____
_____
_____
_____
_____

4. Reread the description in this chapter of my research on AIDS awareness among homeless shelter users. Propose a more ambitious multimethod study of the same research question. Identify the advantages of your design over my original one and highlight the ways in which your use of multiple methods is likely to improve the validity of your measures, causal conclusions, and generalizations. [203–208]

Mini-Projects

Is There a Better Way?

You are to consider whether a research study might have been conducted with other methods and whether this might have altered the conclusions.

1. Identify a researcher to interview about a social science research project he or she directed. This person might be a professor at your school or a member of a research department at some other organization.

2. After introducing yourself and securing the researcher's approval, ask him or her about the research question investigated, the methods used, and the conclusions of the research. Review the list of questions for critiquing a research article for more ideas. Also ask what problems occurred in conducting the research and what important aspects of the research question remain unanswered. What, if any, lessons did the researcher learn about research design?

3. Write a short proposal for a study of the same research question using an alternative research strategy that you think might have yielded different insights about or better answers to the research question. This alternative might involve a different type of sample, different types of measures, and a different approach to establishing causality.

4. Explain the advantages of your alternative approach. Which of the "15 Lessons about Research Design" (text pp. 210–214) do these advantages reflect? Can you propose any other lessons at this point?

Learning by Reading and Comparing

Focus your attention on a research question that has been the subject of numerous empirical investigations in your major field. Perhaps influences on recidivism among persons convicted of crimes, the impact of divorce on children, or differences between private and public schools.

1. Search the literature to find four to five recent articles about this research question that present results from research by different researchers.

2. Read the articles, jotting down brief answers to questions 1–20 from Exhibit 6.1 (text pp. 192–193).

3. Review the 15 research design lessons (text pp. 210–214). Find examples for as many of these lessons as possible in your research articles. Explain why you consider each example to exemplify one or more of these lessons.

4. Note any information in the articles that seems to contradict a research design lesson. Do you think the original lesson needs to be modified or discarded? Explain.

5. Identify any additional lessons that are suggested by these research articles.

6. Summarize what this mini-project has added to your understanding of the research process.

A Pre-Proposal for Research

You will develop a preliminary research proposal that incorporates the portions of the research process that are the focus of chapters 1–6.

1. Formulate a problem for research, adhering to the criteria for good research questions identified in chapter 2 (and explaining, at some point, why you think you have met these criteria). The research problem can be your own invention or it can be based on the social science literature. Express the problem as a question and elaborate on it in one paragraph. State at least two variables involved in the problem and present at least one hypothesis involving these two variables.

2. Outline a plan for conducting research on the research problem. The research plan can involve either individuals or groups (any aggregate) as the units of analysis and collection of either cross-sectional data or longitudinal data, but these aspects of the design should be chosen so as to maximize the strength of the hypothesis test. Be sure that you make your intended units of analysis and the longitudinal nature of the design clear.

3. Propose specific measures for two variables in at least one hypothesis, writing out the actual questions or other instruments you will use. Detail the sampling plan. Explain how you will be able to establish valid conclusions with your design, and indicate whether the design is to be experimental or nonexperimental.

4. Evaluate the relevance of each ethical guideline for your proposed study. Explain how you will handle any problems that arise in the treatment of human subjects. Give a rationale for going ahead with your study in spite of whatever ethical problems you have identified.

7 Experiments

Contamination
Treatment Misidentification
Generalizability
    Sample Generalizability
    External Validity
    Interaction of Testing and Treatment

Issues in Ethical Practice

Deception

Distribution of Benefits

Conclusions

■ ■ ■ ■   Text Objectives

1. Explain the reason for each of the criteria for establishing the existence of a causal relationship.

2. Understand the difference between and benefits of random assignment, random selection, and matching.

3. Distinguish experimental, quasi-experimental, and nonexperimental research designs.

4. Identify the presence or absence of components of true experiments in research designs.

5. List the sources of internal and external validity and know whether they may occur in particular research designs.

6. Determine whether process analysis is likely to be needed in an experimental design and know its role in avoiding treatment misidentification.

7. Describe experimental treatments in which a placebo effect is likely.

8. Compare and contrast the concepts of sample generalizability, external validity, and crosspopulation generalizability.

9. Diagram the essential components of any quantitative research design with simple, standard notation.

10. Debate effectively the ethical problems posed by an experimental design.

Research in the News

1. Can welfare payments be used to produce behavioral change among recipients? The Manpower Demonstration Research Corporation conducted an experiment to begin to answer this politically charged question (Jason DeParle, "Ohio Welfare Bonuses Keep Teen-age Mothers in School." *The New York Times*, April 12, 1993: A14). MDRC studied an Ohio program that gave teenage mothers on welfare additional financial bonuses if they attend school—and deducted this bonus if they dropped out. During the 18-month study of 7,000 teenage mothers, 47% of the previous high school dropouts who received the bonus returned to school, compared to 33% of those who did not receive the bonus. The researchers concluded that the program increased school participation.

The research results were immediately subject to various criticisms and qualifications. Advocates for welfare recipients pointed out that the many eligible mothers who did not return to school simply received less money because of the program. Since the program involved case managers for recipients, it was argued that it was the case manager contact, not the reduced benefits, that changed recipient behavior. The MDRC president herself cautioned that the apparent program effects might not apply to efforts to change such intensely personal decisions as marrying or having children.

Which of these issues are matters of research design? What are the specific research design issues being raised? What other possible problems might invalidate the research? What else would you like to know about the research design in order to evaluate the internal validity of the conclusions? What factors would you consider in evaluating the generalizability of the findings? What are the ethical issues in research like this? [242–258]

_____
_____
_____
_____
_____
_____
_____
_____
_____
_____
_____

2. In August 1993, the state of New Jersey stopped giving additional payments to women who had more children while they were on welfare ("N.J. Welfare Cap Defies Reckoning." *Boston Globe,* June 9, 1996: 24). The policy attempted to use welfare payments to change a more personal behavior than going to school: having children.

But did it work as intended? State data showed a 12% reduction in the birthrate for welfare mothers. However, social researchers reported no difference in the birthrate of welfare mothers who were subjected to the new policy and those who were not. The agency official responsible for the evaluation concluded that it was not clear if the reduction in birthrates was due to "the family cap or something in the water or anything in between."

What additional information would you like to have about this social experiment before evaluating the findings? What would you like to add to the research design to improve its internal validity? Its generalizability? What has this experiment added to what was learned in the welfare experiment on teenage mothers and schooling? [220–235, 242–258]

_____
_____
_____
_____
_____

_____
_____
_____
_____
_____
_____
_____
_____
_____
_____
_____

3. The warning not to drink and drive is common on college campuses (and all too necessary, wouldn't you say?). But how often do you hear warnings about the hazards of combining drugs and driving? A study by Memphis police indicated that it's a serious problem ("Experiment in Memphis Suggests Many Drive after Using Drugs." _The New York Times_, August 28, 1994: 30).

Memphis police outfitted a "drug van" to permit roadside urine tests for drugs. They then gave drug tests to any driver who was driving recklessly but did not seem to be drunk. About 59% of 150 drivers tested in this way seemed to have been using cocaine or marijuana. Cocaine use leads to gross overconfidence in one's abilities, resulting in high-speed driving and frequent lane changes. Marijuana use slows reflexes.

What type of research design did this "experiment" use? What research question did it answer? Can you devise a true experiment or a quasi-experiment that would test the effect of (illegal) drugs on driving? That reasonable people could accept as ethical? [220–242]

_____
_____
_____
_____
_____
_____

Short Essay Questions

1. Discuss the advantages and disadvantages of randomization for achieving valid research results. [222–225]

_____

_____

_____

_____

_____

_____

_____

_____

_____

_____

2. Diagram a simple before-and-after panel design, an ex post facto control group design, a repeated measures panel design, and a nonequivalent control group design (with before-the-fact designation of the groups). Which of these designs is considered quasi-experimental and why? [221–242]

_____

_____

_____

_____

_____

_____

_____

_____

_____

_____

_____

_____

_____

_____

_____

_____

3. What determines the degree of confidence you can place in the internal validity of conclusions from a true experiment? Give examples of ways in which internal validity can be threatened in a true experiment and explain how these threats can be avoided. [242–249]

_____

_____

_____

_____

_____

_____

_____

_____

_____

_____

_____

_____

_____

_____

4. Explain the differences between the concepts of sample generalizability, external validity, and cross-population generalizability. Describe a research design that would maximize the likelihood of generalizability in all three ways. Point out constraints on the utility of such a design.[249–253]

5. A field experiment with a randomized design will study the effects of requiring welfare recipients to work after two years. The recipients will not be told that their work requirements will be assigned randomly. What might such a design consist of? Evaluate the ethics of random assignment and of subject deception in this situation. How could these problems be lessened within the context of an experimental design? [253–258]

_____

_____

_____

_____

_____

_____

_____

_____

_____

_____

_____

_____

Multiple-Choice Questions

1. A psychology lecturer has students answer a set of questions about mental illness at the start of her class. She then flips a coin for each student, sending those whose toss is a head to another room for the rest of the class period. The students who received a tail stay in their original classroom and listen to a talk by a person whose symptoms of schizophrenia remitted after several months on the antipsychotic drug, Clozapin. The students in the other classroom study quietly during the class period. At the end of the period, all the students answer the set of questions about mental illness. Before the class breaks up, a research assistant interviews the students who listened to the talk to learn more about how they reacted to it. Which component of experimental design is the research assistant focusing on? [221]

    a. pretest
    b. randomization
    c. experimental and comparison group
    d. control over conditions
    e. causal mechanism

2. A researcher investigates the impact of a treatment program on alcohol abusers. He assigns alcoholics seeking treatment, using a coin toss, either to participate in the three-day treatment program or to go to a regular hospital ward where they can play checkers, read, and wait for an opening in the program. The researcher has field researchers observe the treatment program and the hospital ward throughout the study. Alcohol use is measured among all study subjects at the end of the three days. What role does the field researcher play in this research design? [221–227]

    a. conducting the posttest
    b. monitoring control over conditions
    c. identifying the causal mechanism
    d. constructing a "post hoc" comparison group
    e. validating the outcome measure

3. What experimental or quasi-experimental design is diagrammed in the box below? [233–235, 252–253]

$$O_1 \times O_2$$

    a. randomized comparative change design
    b. randomized comparative posttest design
    c. nonequivalent control group design
    d. before-and-after design
    e. Solomon 4-group design

4. A sociologist studies the effect of admitting women to a traditionally all-male military school. For the study, she selects two traditional military schools that are of comparable size, have comparable admission requirements and costs, and attract a similar type of student. One of these schools is soon to begin admitting women. She obtains academic aptitude test scores for all the men in both schools before the one school starts admitting women. One year after women are admitted to the one college, the sociologist again obtains academic aptitude test scores for men at both schools. She compares the changes in test scores at both schools to determine whether there is any academic effect of the one school admitting women. Her study design would be termed a _____. [233–239]

    a. randomized comparative change design
    b. randomized comparative posttest design
    c. nonequivalent control group design
    d. before-and-after design
    e. ex post facto control group design.

5. Scandinavians are to lose their universal health care plan in two years. One year before the plan termination date, a study is designed to evaluate the impact of the loss of universal health care on Scandinavians' health. Of the following designs, the one that would be feasible in this situation and also provide the greatest support for conclusions about causality is _____. [233–240]

    a. randomized comparative change design
    b. randomized comparative posttest design
    c. repeated measures panel design
    d. nonequivalent control group design
    e. ex post facto control group design

6. A field experiment is carried out to test the effect of incarceration on recidivism among drug abusers. For the experiment, convicted drug abusers are randomly assigned to incarceration or to probation. All individuals are interviewed by a research assistant prior to assignment. After the interview, a corrections official tosses a coin to determine whether the assignment will be to incarceration or probation. Because he is familiar with some of the convicts, the official "fudges" a few placements so that he can send prisoners he thinks are truly incorrigible to prison while referring a few whom he likes to probation. This creates a threat to internal validity known as _____. [242–247]

    a. differential attrition
    b. testing
    c. compensatory rivalry
    d. regression
    e. selection bias

7. Students are recruited at a Conservative Union to listen to a lecture on the history of patriotism. After the lecture, they fill out a questionnaire that measures the strength of their patriotic feelings. A reduction in patriotism is observed, rather than an increase. So the researcher repeats the study, this time recruiting students from the general student body. What threat to internal validity is the researcher trying to remove by the change in recruitment procedures? [244–247]

a. regression
b. testing
c. maturation
d. history
e. contamination

8. Student volunteers come to a gym for a study of the value of exercise. A research assistant announces that half the students will remain in this gym and half will be selected, randomly, to exercise in another gym with new, high-tech exercise equipment. The students spend two hours exercising. The two gyms are arranged identically except for the high-tech equipment used by the students in one group; conditions are carefully controlled. Students reconvene together in the original gym at the end of the exercise period before filling out a questionnaire about the value of exercise. Causal conclusions from this experiment may be invalid due to _____. [242–247]

a. selection bias
b. testing
c. regression
d. history
e. compensatory rivalry

9. Similar experiments are conducted at two different large offices, PMX and Riverside. At both offices, volunteers are assigned randomly to separate rooms, where they either read a manual on using the World Wide Web to improve productivity (in one room) or sit quietly for two hours without reading (in the other room). The only difference in procedures is that at PMX, subjects in both rooms take a break after one hour and socialize all together in the hall. Which research design minimizes threats to internal validity and why? [242–247]

a. PMX is superior due to less threat of selection bias.
b. Riverside is superior due to less threat of regression.
c. The designs are identical in terms of possible threats to internal validity.
d. Riverside is superior due to less threat of demoralization.
e. PMX is superior due to less threat of history.

10. In an experiment on the effects of dieting on eating disorders among all persons at a weight-watch clinic, it is determined that dieting increased eating disorders for people who were only mildly overweight, but not for those who were severely obese. It would be said that the conclusion that dieting increases eating disorders is _____. [242, 248–252]

    a. generalizable
    b. not valid
    c. internally valid
    d. a product of the experimental arrangements
    e. not externally valid

11. Students at a large commuter college are randomly sampled. A random half of those sampled are then sent an information packet about student health benefits. The rest are sent nothing. Two months later, all the students in the random sample are sent a questionnaire to measure their knowledge about health benefits. The same proportion of students return the questionnaire whether or not they received the information packet. The average knowledge level of both groups is the same. However, the research design precludes confidence that the conclusion that "college student knowledge about health benefits is not influenced by receipt of an information packet" is _____. [242–253]

    a. generalizable to other colleges
    b. appropriate in a causal sense
    c. internally valid
    d. generalizable to the staff at the college studied
    e. based on a longitudinal design

Mini-Projects

A Litter Experiment

This is a simple experiment to test the hypothesis that wastebaskets reduce litter. It could generate big problems if you're not conscientious. Be sure that you've reviewed arrangements with your instructor and that you pick up *all* the hallway litter after the experiment is over.

1. Pick a corridor in a campus building that meets the following specifications: all the rooms off the corridor are classrooms; the corridor is used by many students; the classes in these rooms begin at the same time; and the corridor is relatively quiet while classes are in session. Instead of a corridor you could use the rotunda in a large building with lecture halls off the rotunda.

2. Arrange with campus maintenance to have four wastebaskets that you can use in the hallway on one day. Your instructor can inform the maintenance department that this is for a study of how to reduce litter.

3. Prepare several hundred flyers that publicize a public on-campus activity in which a student in your class is involved (with the consent of the student)—perhaps a concert, a lecture, or an open meeting. But keep the flyer fairly boring: no snazzy fonts or snappy pictures.

4. On the day of the experiment, start by getting any wastebaskets out of the corridor and out of sight. If there are permanent waste receptacles, see if you can arrange to tape an OUT OF ORDER sign over them.

5. About 20 minutes before the passing period, station at least two students at both ends of the hallway and at every intersecting corridor. Each student should carry a stack of flyers and try to give one to every passing student.

6. After the passing period has ended and the hallway is relatively clear, walk down the corridor and pick up every flyer. Count the number of flyers discarded on the floor.

7. Before the next passing period, place the four (or more) wastebaskets in the hall in locations that are as visible as possible. Then repeat steps 5–6.

8. Now repeat the entire procedure, steps 4–7, at least one more time. Be sure that every time you repeat the procedure you begin distributing flyers at exactly the same time before the next class sessions.

9. Tally the number of flyers picked up off the floor during the periods when wastebaskets were present, and when they were not.

10. Did the experimental treatment (wastebaskets) appear to have had any effect in reducing litter? How well were the experimental procedures implemented? What changes in the experimental procedures would you recommend for a stronger test of the hypothesis? What do you think are the

limits of generalizability of your findings? Are there some groups, or situations, in which you think that your treatment wouldn't work? (Or, if there was no effect, where it would work?)

Charitable Giving

Pick a charity that you feel is deserving of support. If multiple students participate in this project, try to reach a consensus about which charity this should be. It would help if you, your instructor, or another student already have some contact with the charity. The experiment will be most interesting if you team up with two other students, one male and one female.

1. Call or visit an official at the charity, explain your project, and secure the charity's permission before you carry out the experiment. Ask them for any brochures or other material they would like you to distribute.

2. Check with campus police (or city or town police, if you carry out the experiment off campus) about solicitation laws. Be sure not to violate these laws (modify the suggested procedures if necessary).

3. Station yourself at a location outdoors where many people pass by during the day, perhaps during lunch hour. Hold a cup and a sign that asks for contributions to the charity. Simply thank people for their contributions. (If you get any!)

4. Continue for one hour then count up your contributions.

5. Now change your "experimental treatment." A student of the other gender might replace you, or you might change to a markedly different charity (from battered women to veterans, for example, or Boy Scouts).

6. Repeat steps 3–4 at the same time on another day.

7. Repeat the entire cycle.

8. Add up the amount of money you received with each different experimental treatment.

9. The experimental design can be enriched by having an observer calculate the percentage of women and men passing by who contribute with the two different treatments.

10. Did contributions vary with the experimental manipulation? How well were the experimental procedures implemented? What changes in the experimental procedures would you recommend for a stronger test of the hypothesis? What do you think are the limits of generalizability of your findings? Did the treatment effect (or noneffect) occur for both women and men? Are there some other groups, or situations, in which you think your treatment wouldn't work? (Or, if there was no effect, where it would work?)

Going to the Movies

This project is relatively easy to carry out, but you have to prepare carefully for it.

1. Arrange with an instructor in a large class to conduct a before-and-after study of the impact of watching a regularly scheduled class movie. Ask the instructor about what the students are to learn from the movie. Also check to make sure that the movie is no longer than the class period. Preferably it will be shorter, so that you can administer a short test before and after the movie.

2. Watch the movie yourself, at least several days before it is to be shown to the class. Take notes. Review your notes and the instructor's goals for the movie, then develop a short test to measure knowledge or feelings about the topics in the film. Ask your methods instructor and the course instructor to review your test.

3. Administer the test to some of the students in your methods class and ask them for feedback on the questions. Revise the test to eliminate ambiguity and other sources of confusion in the wording of questions and answers.

4. For a more interesting analysis, include in your test a question(s) to measure some characteristic that might be related to differences in sensitivity to the film. Gender, race, or age might work. Keep it simple.

5. Administer the test shortly before and after the film is shown. If there won't be time to do all this in one class, administer the pretest at the end of the preceding class and the beginning of the next class. If possible, administer the test again one week after the movie was shown.

6. Score the knowledge or feelings test. Tally up the scores, together with responses to any other questions you included (such as gender, race, or age).

7. Calculate the average score for before and after the film. Then calculate separate before-and-after scores for the groups defined by other variables you measured (if age is one of them, just collapse the values down to "old" (relatively) and "young").

8. Describe the apparent immediate and long-term impacts of the movie on knowledge. Did the immediate impact, if any, diminish over time? Did the immediate impact vary across any student characteristics you measured? What changes in experimental procedures would you recommend at this point? What are the likely sources of internal invalidity? How generalizable do you think the findings are?

Name: _____ **Date:** _____ **Instructor:** _____

Exploring the General Social Survey

1. A brief exercise can illustrate the process of analyzing experimental data, although we have only survey data to work with. Assume, though, that individuals are assigned randomly to attend no more than 12 years of school or to attend school at least through the 13th year. The hypothesis for the experiment is that those with at least 13 years of education will have a larger vocabulary than those with no more than 12 years of education.

2. The "t-test" statistic can be used to test this hypothesis.

```
TEMPORARY.
RECODE EDUC(0 THRU 12=1)(13 THRU HI=2).
T-TEST GROUPS=EDUC(1,2)/VARS=WORDSUM.
```

Inspect the "Group Statistics" table. You can see that the mean number of words correct was higher for those with at least 13 years of school (6.93) than for those with less school (5.35). Now look at the "Independent Samples Test" table. In the "sig." (for significance) column, we see that the "t-test for equality of means" reveals a difference in means that is significant at the .001 level. The mean difference in vocabulary between the two groups would occur on the basis of chance alone less than one-tenth of 1% of the time. So our hypothesis is supported.

3. Now, recognizing that this did not involve an experimental design, list a few of the possible explanations for the vocabulary difference that do not involve a causal effect of education on vocabulary. Think about the possibility of an alternative time order of effects and consider at least two possible extraneous variables. [117–124]

_____

_____

_____

_____

_____

_____

_____

_____

8 Survey Research

Surveys by Telephone
In-Person Interviews
A Comparison of Survey Designs
Issues in Ethical Practice
Conclusions

■ ■ ■ ■ **Text Objectives**

1. Understand the reasons for the popularity of survey research and the problems due to its popularity.

2. Design a survey instrument around a single research question.

3. Identify common errors made in writing survey questions and reasons for using closed-ended and open-ended questions.

4. Write an effective and ethical cover letter for a mailed survey.

5. Specify the situations for which four different types of surveys are appropriate.

Research in the News

1. The International Gallup Poll surveyed attitudes toward gender roles in 22 countries (Tamar Lewin, "Americans Attached to Traditional Roles for Sexes, Poll Finds." *The New York Times,* March 27, 1996: A15). In each country, interviews were conducted with a representative sample of about 1,000 adults. The strongest support for traditional gender roles in the family was found in Hungary, where two-thirds of the respondents felt that a working father and a stay-at-home mother was the ideal family structure. About half of Americans, Chileans, French, and Japanese idealized this traditional family structure, compared to one-fourth in Germany, India, Lithuania, Spain, Taiwan, and Thailand.

There were some similarities but even more differences in other gender role-related attitudes between countries. Around the world, men and women both perceived women as more emotional, talkative, and affectionate than men, who were seen as more courageous, aggressive and ambitious. Belief in the equal intelligence of men and women was widespread, as was a belief that they should have equal opportunities. Women political leaders tended to be seen in a positive light, but men tended to be preferred as bosses in the workplace.

What do these international results add to your understanding of attitudes about gender roles? Would you suggest attention to any particular issues in evaluating measurement validity in this cross-cultural research? What additional variables would you suggest should be measured in order to explain these differences between countries? The Gallup Organization reported the margin of sampling error for each country's data as plus or minus three percentage points. What does this mean? [177–180]

_____

_____

_____

_____

_____

_____

_____

_____

_____

_____

_____

_____

_____

_____

_____

_____

_____

2. A 1993 Louis Harris survey conducted for the Harvard School of Public Health revealed that 90% of American adults backed the Brady bill, to require a waiting period and background checks in connection with handgun purchases (Felicity Barringer, "Majority in Poll Back Ban on Handguns." *The New York Times,* June 4, 1993: A14). About 80% felt that the easy availability of so many guns helps to create an atmosphere of violence. About one-third knew a child who had accidentally shot himself or herself or had been shot by another child.

Support for handgun control seemed to be increasing. In 1991, 41% of Americans polled favored a ban on handguns (except when a court granted an exception); in 1993, 52% supported a ban. Support for handgun control was higher among women polled (61%) than among men (42%). The percent of households owning guns had declined from 45% in 1989 to 42% in 1993—the first decline in two decades. However, a spokesman for the National Rifle Association pointed to the increasing involvement of youth in the drug trade, not guns themselves, as the problem.

What else do you need to know about the poll in order to assess the generalizability of its findings? The validity of its measures? Do you need any other information before concluding that attitudes had changed since 1991, or that gun ownership had declined since 1989? What might explain these changes? How could you evaluate empirically the impact of knowing children who had been hurt by guns on support for a handgun ban? Of the use of youth in the drug trade on the frequency of child injury by guns? What do you think explains the different attitudes of men and women? What additional variables would you need to measure to test your explanation? What role do you think results of such polls should play in the political arena? What about the practice termed "governing by the polls"— that is, shaping government policy to fit the preferences of a majority of citizens (or eligible voters)? [268–272]

_____

_____

_____

_____

_____

_____

_____

_____

_____

_____

_____

_____

_____

_____

_____

_____

_____

_____

_____

_____

_____

_____

3. When is a poll not a poll? Some political campaigns have been using "push polls" to increase support for their candidate. These polls are not surveys with a goal of obtaining valid, generalizable information, but partisan efforts to spread false information that masquerade as professional polls. Professional pollsters from both the Democratic and Republican parties have spoken out against the practice (Adam Clymer, "Association of Political Handlers Attacks Ruse Polls as Unethical." *The New York Times,* June 27, 1996: A20).

How could it be determined that a poll is a push poll rather than a legitimate poll to learn about public opinion? Which ethical principles are violated by push polls? What types of questions and statements concerning opposing candidates do you think should be excluded from political polls?

What types could be seen as legitimate? Would you suggest any additions to the American Sociological Association's *Code of Ethics* (see the text, p. 59) to counter push polling? [301–303]

_____

_____

_____

_____

_____

_____

_____

_____

_____

_____

_____

_____

_____

_____

Short Essay Questions

1. Illustrate each of the five types of interpretive questions. Write the questions to help interpret answers to the question, "How safe is your community?" [274–275]

_____

_____

_____

_____

_____

_____

_____

_____

_____

_____

_____

2. Are surveys too easy to conduct? Compare the advantages and disadvantages of surveys. Give an example of a research question for which a survey design would be markedly inferior to another design. [270–272]

_____

_____

_____

_____

_____

_____

_____

_____

_____

_____

_____

_____

_____

_____

3. Studying sensitive topics like sexuality requires special care in survey design. Discuss those guidelines for writing individual questions that would be of particular concern when dealing with sensitive topics. Indicate whether you would prefer open-ended or closed-ended response formats and whether you would include neutral and "don't know" response options. Explain your reasoning. [280–283]

_____

_____

_____

_____

_____

_____

_____

_____

_____

_____

_____

_____

4. Review the procedures for maximizing the response rate to a mailed questionnaire. Include a discussion of the contents and format of the cover letter as well as other elements of survey preparation and distribution. [289–292]

_____
_____
_____
_____
_____
_____
_____
_____
_____
_____
_____
_____
_____

5. A researcher is to study the attitudes of adult Americans toward drug abuse. Discuss the advantages and disadvantages of using in-person, mailed, and phone surveys for this study. [289–300]

_____
_____
_____
_____
_____
_____
_____
_____
_____
_____
_____
_____
_____
_____

Multiple-Choice Questions

1. Bob Carruthers designs a questionnaire on attitudes toward punishment and plans to mail it out to a random sample. He began to design the questionnaire by specifying clearly his objectives: to determine the level of support for severe forms of punishment as well as the sources of this support. He developed questions to measure substantive variables that had to do with this problem as well as many questions designed to interpret the answers to the important substantive questions. What step, if any, has he left out of the process of question design? [272–275]

   a. developing a guiding framework
   b. finding out what respondents know about juries
   c. consulting with other people
   d. selecting the dependent variables
   e. No steps have been left out.

Questions 2–8 refer to the specific questions highlighted from a hypothetical questionnaire. The questionnaire was designed to assess the reactions of nonvoters in an Eastern city to a "get out the vote" campaign.

---

2. How many reminders have you seen in the last two months to register to vote?
   a. NOT MANY
   b. A FEW
   c. SOME
   d. A LOT

---

2. Which, if any, guideline for writing individual questions identifies the main problem in the preceding question and/or its response choices? [275–283]

   a. Avoid making disagreement disagreeable.
   b. Minimize the risk of bias.
   c. Make questions and response choices clear.
   d. Focus on one issue.
   e. Minimize fence-sitting.

> 3. Do you think the campaign to get the vote sponsored by the Mayor and other distinguished officials was a good idea?
>   a. YES
>   b. NOT SURE
>   c. NO

3. Which, if any, guideline for writing individual questions identifies the main problem in the preceding question and/or its response choices? [275–283]

   a. Avoid making disagreement disagreeable.
   b. Minimize the risk of bias.
   c. Make questions and response choices clear.
   d. Focus on one issue.
   e. Minimize floating.

> 4. Do you think it is possible or impossible that there was never any reason to have a "get out the vote" campaign?
>   a. YES
>   b. NO

4. Which, if any, guideline for writing individual questions identifies the main problem in the preceding question and/or its response choices? [275–283]

   a. Avoid making disagreement disagreeable.
   b. Minimize the risk of bias.
   c. Make questions and response choices clear.
   d. Focus on one issue.
   e. Minimize floating.

> 5. Are you satisfied or dissatisfied with how the campaign to increase votes was carried out?
>   a. SATISFIED
>   b. DISSATISFIED

5. Which, if any, guideline for writing individual questions identifies the main problem in the preceding question and/or its response choices? [275–283]

   a. Avoid making disagreement disagreeable.
   b. Minimize the risk of bias.
   c. Make questions and response choices clear.
   d. Focus on one issue.
   e. Minimize floating.

6. Elected officials are to blame for the frequency of nonvoting.
   a. AGREE
   b. NEITHER AGREE NOR DISAGREE
   c. DISAGREE

6. Which, if any, guideline for writing individual questions identifies the main problem in the preceding question and/or its response choices? [275–283]

   a. Avoid making disagreement disagreeable.
   b. Minimize the risk of bias.
   c. Make questions and response choices clear.
   d. Focus on one issue.
   e. Minimize floating.

7. To what extent do you agree or disagree with the following statement? There should be more than one way for people to express their political preferences through voting.
   a. STRONGLY AGREE
   b. AGREE
   c. NEITHER AGREE NOR DISAGREE
   d. DISAGREE
   e. STRONGLY DISAGREE

7. Which, if any, guideline for writing individual questions identifies the main problem in the preceding question and/or its response choices? [275–283]

   a. Avoid making disagreement disagreeable.
   b. Minimize the risk of bias.
   c. Make questions and response choices clear.
   d. Focus on one issue.
   e. Minimize floating.

8. Do you think the candidates are uninteresting and the parties are indistinguishable?
   a. YES
   b. MAYBE
   c. NO

8. Which, if any, guideline for writing individual questions identifies the main problem in the preceding question and/or its response choices? [275–283]

    a. Avoid making disagreement disagreeable.
    b. Minimize the risk of bias.
    c. Make questions and response choices clear.
    d. Focus on one issue.
    e. Minimize floating.

9. Survey Consultants must design a survey with many questions, some of them complex with multiple branches and some of them of little interest to respondents. The questions do not tend to deal with personal or intimate matters. What would be the most advantageous survey design for achieving these goals? [287–299]

    a. mailed self-administered questionnaire
    b. group-administered questionnaire
    c. phone survey
    d. structured in-person interviews
    e. unstructured in-person interviews

10. Professor Sandolsin must design a survey of a local factory. The survey must include many questions about issues of concern to spouses, including satisfaction with the rate of pay and the child care arrangements they prefer. It is important that the survey results be generalizable to the entire population of spouses in the community, but the factory does not have very much money for the survey. What would be the most advantageous survey design for achieving these goals? [287–299]

    a. mailed self-administered questionnaire
    b. group-administered questionnaire
    c. phone survey
    d. structured in-person interviews
    e. unstructured in-person interviews

Mini-Projects

A Survey Replication

The goal of this project is to gain experience in the mechanics of survey research without spending the time to write original questions.

1. Review the variables in the 1994 General Social Survey. Select an area of interest that corresponds to a subset of questions in the GSS and that is relevant to a group to which you can easily administer a survey. The latter might include students in a class, colleagues at work, or members of a voluntary organization in which you are involved (maybe even participants in a large family gathering).

2. Obtain the original GSS questions in this subset (your instructor can call the National Opinion Research Center in Chicago for a copy of the entire survey), or visit the GSS web site (http://www.icpsr.vmich.edv.gss/).

3. Review the questions and add additional questions about related issues of interest or to improve the flow of the questionnaire. Keep the length of the total instrument to just two pages.

4. Write a short, one-paragraph introductory statement and make arrangements for distributing and collecting the survey in one time period.

5. Administer the survey. Be sure to explain why you are conducting the survey and why the group should find it to be of interest. Also take careful note of how many persons are present and how many do not complete the questionnaire.

6. Tally up the responses to each question. Convert to percentages.

7. Generate the percentage distributions for responses to the same questions in the 1994 GSS. (You may need to wait until you have completed chapter 11 before you do this.)

8. Compare the distribution of responses in your selected group to those of the general population, as reflected in the 1994 GSS. How similar or different are the attitudes? What might account for the differences?

Open or Closed Questions?

Any decision about research design involves trade-offs and compromises between such goals as achieving measurement reliability and validity, generalizability, and cost-effectiveness. This project focuses on one such trade-off: the decision to use open- or closed-ended questions.

1. Begin by formulating a research question that is appropriate for a survey of college students. Identify at least one hypothesis and several variables that are involved in this question.

2. Draft 12 closed-ended questions that measure these variables. Some questions may be part of an index; some may be alternative measures of the same variable. For a shorter project, select your questions (and the research question), from the General Social Survey or another instrument to which you have access.

3. Circulate your questions to classmates for critique. Consider carefully their comments and revise your questions as seems warranted.

4. Now write three to four open-ended questions that you think will measure the same variables as the closed-ended questions. Circulate your questions to classmates for critique and revise as seems warranted.

5. Prepare the closed-ended questions as a short questionnaire and the open-ended questions as a short interview schedule.

6. Administer the forced-choice version of the survey to five other students in a cafeteria or lounge. It will be easiest to do this one student at a time, rather than in a group. Ask each student to answer all the survey questions while you wait. Collect their survey sheet.

7. Now interview each student using the interview schedule containing the open-ended questions. Explain that you will be going back over the same issues, but with somewhat different questions. Record their responses verbatim, in a spiral-bound notebook.

8. Ask your respondents whether they provided different information in response to the interview than in the questionnaire. If they perceive any such difference, ask them to explain. Then thank your respondents.

9. Compare responses to the open-ended and closed-ended questions. Prepare a summary sheet that indicates the differences you found for each respondent. Write a short report on the differences and similarities. What changes would you make in the closed-ended questions based on the open-ended responses? Has your confidence in closed-ended questions been increased or decreased? Explain.

A Split-Ballot Experiment by Telephone

Many people (myself among them) are fed up with telemarketing and other phone solicitations. So plan this survey exercise carefully. Keep the instrument very short and interesting. Be very pleasant on the phone no matter what response you get to your request for an interview. And be prepared to say, "Thank you anyway. I'm sorry I bothered you" if they refuse.

1. Select a topic for a short phone survey. This might be a current issue in the news or a general concern in the community. For the purposes of this exercise, avoid topics that are very emotionally charged, such as terrorist bombings or abortion rights.

2. Pose one or more hypotheses about possible influences on attitudes about this issue or concern (perhaps "Strength of support for lower taxes will increase with age," or "Women will support more spending for the public schools than will men").

3. Write about 10 questions that measure the variables in your hypothesis(es).

4. Organize your questions into a logical flow and pretest them on some classmates.

5. Develop a brief introductory statement that states the focus of your survey, its auspices (a class project at your college or university), and its length (hopefully only a few minutes). Your statement should include the request that you would like to speak to any adult in the household. Try this out on a few friends and make whatever revisions seem warranted.

6. Select one or more communities in which you will conduct your phone survey and determine the corresponding phone exchange(s). Devise a scheme to sample randomly the appropriate range of phone numbers, using the table of random numbers in appendix 4 (text p. 518). Pick about 50 random phone numbers, with a goal of completing 10 interviews.

7. Start making calls from your list until you are able to complete 10 interviews with an adult at a residence. Whenever you reach a business, apologize, explain that you were trying to reach someone else, and hang up.

8. Describe your experiences in a short paper. Report on the number of calls answered, the number that reached a household, the number that reached an adult, the number (and percentage) of refusals, and the responses to your survey questions. What have you learned about phone interviewing? Which survey questions seem to need improvement?

Exploring the General Social Survey

1. Try your hand at recoding several variables so that you are able to meet the requirements of different statistical analyses. Change labor force status to a dichotomy that distinguishes those in the labor force from those not in the labor force. Change marital status so as to treat divorced and separated persons similarly. Group country of family origin responses into a limited number of categories. Begin by generating the unrecoded frequency distributions of these variables. [512–515]

```
FREQUENCIES WRKSTAT,MARITAL,ETHNIC.
```

2. Now write a recode statement for each of these variables. [501–502]

```
RECODE WRKSTAT (1,2,3,4=1)(5,6,7,8=2).
VALUE LABELS WRKSTAT 1 'In labor force' 2 'Not in
     labor force'.
RECODE MARITAL (1,2=1)(3,4=2)(5=3).
VALUE LABELS MARITAL 1 'SUCCESSFULLY MARRIED' 2
     'UNSUCCESSFULLY MARRIED' 3 'NEVER MARRIED'.
RECODE ETHNIC (1=1)(2,7,8,9,10,11,12,14,15,18,19,
     24,25,26,27,36,41=2)(...
VALUE LABELS ETHNIC 1 'AFRICA' 2 'WESTERN EUROPE'
     3....
```

_____

_____

_____

_____

_____

3. Generate the recoded frequency distributions. FREQUENCIES WRKSTAT, MARITAL, ETHNIC. Discuss the impact of the recodes. [501–502]

_____

_____

_____

_____

_____

_____

_____

_____

_____

_____

4. Check to see whether minor differences in question wording influence responses. Generate the basic summary statistics for two versions of the same measure that were administered in a split-ballot experiment to random halves of the overall GSS sample.

    DESCRIPTIVES COLAFF,COLAFFY,FUTURUP,FUTURDOWN.

5. Enrich your understanding of answers to a question by examining the relations of those answers to other questions that help to interpret the answers.

    CROSSTABS FAMSUFFR BY SEX, MARITAL, WRKSTAT,
        SATJOB, SPWRKSTA, MAWKBORN/CELLS=COUNT,COL.
    CROSSTABS FAMSUFFR BY MARITAL, WRKSTAT, SATJOB,
        SPWRKSTA, MAWKBORN BY SEX/CELLS=COUNT,COL.

Answer each of the questions on text pp. 274–275 in light of what the above tables reveal. [515–518]

_____

_____

_____

_____

_____

_____

_____

_____

_____

_____

_____

_____

_____

_____

_____

_____

_____

_____

6. Find out how many groups respondents belong to. [502]

```
COUNT GROUPS=MEMFRAT TO MEMOTHER(1).
```

9 Field Research

■ ■ ■ ■ Text Objectives

1. Describe the advantages and disadvantages of a complete participant and a complete observer role in field research.

2. Develop appropriate strategies for entering the field, developing and maintaining relations in the field, sampling, and recording and analyzing data.

3. Conduct an intensive interview and analyze the results.

4. Evaluate the quality of participant observation studies, focus groups, and intensive interviews.

5. Debate the ethical issues posed by diverse field research strategies.

Research in the News

1. Among the staff at Xerox Corporation's Palo Alto Research Center are a team of anthropologists who conduct field research on workers and customers (Claudia H. Deutsch, "Coping with Cultural Polyglots." *The New York Times*, February 24, 1991: F25). One anthropologist observed social interaction at an airport to determine how to increase the efficiency of operations and to make equipment more user-friendly. An Illinois anthropologist started a newsletter to convey anthropological insights into business issues. In one study, he found that some Asian American and Latin American first officers on airplanes tend not to point out hazards to their captain due to a tradition of respecting authority figures.

What field research techniques would you recommend for a study of social interaction in a company you are familiar with as an employee or a customer? What would be the pressures for and against taking the role of complete participant in such a study? What ethical issues arise in research like that reported by the *Times*? [317–324]

2. Workplace culture was also a focus of concern in the U.S. Postal Service in 1989. Work teams were implemented to encourage employee participation in decisions and management attention to employee suggestions (Mary Sit, "Power-sharing: Does It Really Have a Chance?" *Boston Globe*, September 12, 1989: 43). The culture of authoritarian supervision was challenged. In at least some post offices, the results included more efficient and less costly operations and fewer grievances. At Digital Equipment Corporation a similar approach reduced defects in keyboards and increased the ability to meet delivery deadlines.

How does such a strategy for learning about, and changing, organizational culture compare to that represented by the Xerox approach (question 1)? If you managed an organization and wanted to change its culture, would you hire a field researcher or set up work teams? What, if anything, do you think a sociological or anthropological field researcher can contribute to such an effort? What are the similarities and differences between the role of the workers in the work team and the role of a field researcher as a complete participant? [313–324]

3. Is love at least some of what you need? Some social historians have thought that romantic love was a unique development of European medieval culture. Cross-cultural field research by anthropologists suggests otherwise (Daniel Goleman, "After Kinship and Marriage, Anthropology Discovers Love." *The New York Times*, November 24, 1992: C1, C2). A systematic review of field research reports, informant interviews, and folk tales each pointed to the existence of romantic love in the vast majority of 166 human cultures.

What differed between societies was whether romantic love was allowed to determine marital decisions. Many cultures have traditionally expected parents or other authorities to arrange mates for children. Romantic love was left for expression outside of the conjugal unit, or, in some cultures, through marrying an additional wife. In recent years, however, the spread of television and movies across the world has shown many others the importance of romantic love in the United States and other Westernized cultures. One result appears to have been a decline in children's acceptance of arranged marriages.

What sources of evidence could you use in a study of the importance of romantic love in American culture? Where might you conduct your field research? What documents and cultural artifacts would you inspect? What focus groups would you convene and what questions would you ask of them? How would you distinguish marriages on the basis of romantic love from marriages on other bases? Or would you need to? [328–343]

Short Essay Questions

1. If your goal is to maximize measurement validity in a study of social interaction in (legal) riverboat gambling casinos, would you adopt a strategy of complete observation, complete participation, or some mixture of participation and observation? Describe your strategy and explain why you think it is superior to the other strategies for maximizing measurement validity in this situation. [317–324]

_____

_____

_____

_____

_____

_____

_____

_____

_____

_____

_____

_____

_____

_____

2. How ethical is complete participation? Review the ethical guidelines for social research and discuss whether complete participation interferes with, or even prevents, adherence to each of them. Explain when, if ever, you think complete participation might be ethical. [343–345]

_____

_____

_____

_____

_____

_____

_____

_____

_____

_____

_____

_____

_____

_____

_____

3. Compare and contrast the methodology of focus groups and that of intensive interviewing. Indicate their relative advantages and disadvantages. Describe a research question particularly appropriate for each and explain your reasoning. [325–330]

_____

_____

_____

_____

_____

_____

_____

_____

_____

_____

_____

_____

_____

4. Draft instructions for a research assistant who must enter a neighbor-hood bar as a participant observer and then maintain social relations in it. Discuss the personal and scientific problems that must be taken into account in your instructions. [321–324]

5. Field research often results in a detailed description of a limited social setting. However, the resulting books, such as *Tally's Corner,* may be read by a wide audience and used to understand social behavior in many settings. Construct an argument for or against the generalizability of the results of field research studies. Also indicate to what extent you feel it is worthwhile to forgo probability sampling methods to achieve other goals through field research. [313–317]

_____

_____

_____

_____

_____

_____

_____

_____

_____

_____

_____

_____

_____

_____

_____

_____

Multiple-Choice Questions

1. Malia Oznan is a field researcher who studies nonverbal expressions of conflict in casual social situations. She does not drink herself, but she is able to obtain waitress jobs that allow her to observe people socializing in bars. She lets customers think that she is a regular employee and does not mention her research role to anyone connected with the bars. Her note taking is done after hours in her own apartment. Her role as a field researcher is that of a _____. [317–324]

    a. note taker
    b. complete observer
    c. partial observer
    d. complete participant
    e. participant and observer

2. Paul Samuels explains to members of the Hillside Gardening Club that he is a researcher who studies social relations in neighborhood groups. They allow him to attend meetings and interview members whenever mutually agreeable arrangements can be made. He attends meetings frequently, sitting quietly in a back row and taking notes. His role as a field researcher is that of a _____. [317–324]

    a. note taker
    b. complete observer
    c. partial observer
    d. participant and observer
    e. complete participant

3. Celia Satonsky observed group dynamics in an athletic club. She attended group workout sessions and interviewed club members in the lounge. She accompanied members on occasional competitions and attended club parties. She began to wake up thinking about what she could do that day at the club and found herself speaking up for the athletic club when it was criticized by local residents for late-night parties. She promised that her research would help the club to restore its standing in the community. She was _____. [317–324]

    a. successfully playing the role of complete participant
    b. successfully combining observation and participation in her research
    c. using multiple methods to increase the validity of her field research
    d. going native
    e. exemplifying the field research role of complete observation

4. Casual social interaction among employees seems to play a critical role in increasing commitment to the firm. In order to test this hypothesis, a business anthropologist has 25 employees of a large meat-packing plant carry pagers and beeps them at random intervals. At these times, the employees fill out a brief report about what they are doing. This is an example of _____. [334–336]

    a. theoretical sampling
    b. purposive sampling
    c. experience sampling
    d. quota sampling
    e. snowball sampling

Mini-Projects

Social Behavior in Public Places

For this project, you will conduct a short observational study of social behavior in a public place.

1. You may select an outdoor mall, a church service, or some other setting with a large number of people that is open to the public and where you can hang around without appearing too conspicuous. Go to the setting only to conduct this assignment—not because you have business or social plans there.

2. Plan to spend about 20 minutes conducting your study. Allow at least that much time soon afterward to write up your notes (and, of course, more time than that to write the paper). Prepare a tentative plan for observing, emphasizing phenomena that are of most interest to you and that you believe will be most helpful in understanding social behavior at this location. Consider observing the frequency and type of interactions between people, physical arrangements in the location, the number and ages of people, and so on. You should observe nonverbal ties and body language, exits and entrances, spatial arrangement of people, and so on. Also review mentally your previous experiences in this type of setting to help you decide how to focus your formal observational experience.

3. While you are observing, take brief notes as unobtrusively as possible. Depending on the setting, you might want to go outside or to another area to unobtrusively jot down a few notes.

4. Write up your notes in as much detail as possible (try to record all that you observed) soon after leaving the setting (but do not try to record everything "while it is happening"—you'll miss too much). Record what you observed as accurately as possible. Be sure to include in your notes a description of the place that you observed and of the types of people in the setting. Try to focus on the situation, the types of people in it, and how they interact, not on particular individuals or socially irrelevant activities (such as the color of clothes worn). You may try to infer characteristics such as social class and mood from what you observe about people, but be sure and cite the evidence for your inferences.

5. You may wish to count the numbers of activities, persons of different types, and so on. If anyone asks you what you are doing, you should mention that you are observing people's behavior for a class assignment.

6. Begin your research report by identifying the issue(s) that you studied in the setting. In a methods section, describe the setting and draw a map of it. Report briefly on how your "study" developed: how you entered the

setting, what you first noticed in the setting, how you felt in that setting, what you did during the observational period, and what impact you seemed to have in the setting. Present your findings, identifying the different types of behavior and types of interactions and/or groups you observed. Note the frequency of occurrence of these behaviors, how their occurrence varied, and who engaged in which behaviors. Try to identify the similarities and differences between people and groups engaged in different behaviors.

7. Analyze your observations. What have you learned about social behavior in this setting? Are differences in social status or other characteristics important in influencing behavior in this type of setting? In your conclusions, discuss the strengths and weaknesses of your study and explain how generalizable you believe your findings are. What general conclusions about social relations or human behavior can you draw from your study? How effective was your methodology? What hypotheses and methods are suggested for further research? Note any influence that your own orientation toward or role in the setting may have had on your observations and interpretations.

Focusing a Group

Implement the focus group project you designed for exercise 7 (text p. 349).

1. Review your focus group plan carefully. Show it to classmates for helpful suggestions. Write out and rehearse key questions to ask.

2. Recruit six to eight students to participate in a focused discussion of the current event you specified in exercise 7. Reserve a small classroom at a time that is convenient for all group members.

3. Prepare the classroom just before the scheduled meeting, making sure that the tables and chairs are arranged and distractions are removed.

4. Introduce yourself to the focus group members and explain the focus and purpose of the discussion. Ask for consent to take notes or tape-record the discussion but specify that no one's real name will be used in the research report. Let group members introduce themselves.

5. Begin the discussion with an appropriate lead-in question. Continue asking questions when needed and as appropriate. Use a tape recorder or have another student take notes off to the side (if the focus group members have given their consent).

6. Keep track of time and don't let any single student monopolize the discussion. Conclude the period by thanking everyone for their time and thoughts.

7. Write a report on your focus group and suggest improvements that could be made in your questions or in your group management practices.

Social Interaction on the Internet

Use this exercise to practice your intensive interviewing technique and to learn about the difference between social interaction in person and through computers.

1. Identify an acquaintance who uses the Internet for communicating socially with others. This could be another student, a friend, or a family member who regularly visits an online "chat group" or uses e-mail to maintain a regular correspondence with others.

2. Ask the acquaintance if you can watch him or her communicating on the Internet. If this is possible, simply observe for 20–30 minutes to get a sense of the "look and feel" of this communication style. If an observation session is not possible, just continue to step 3.

3. Focus on the quality of social interaction among Internet correspondents. Based in part on what you have observed, prepare a set of general questions to learn about how the respondent communicates on the Internet, who the respondent communicates with and why, how the respondent experiences his or her relations with others on the Internet, and how these relations differ from, or are similar to, the respondent's non-Internet social relations with others.

4. If you have time, ask your respondent for the name of another Internet correspondent and ask that person for an interview.

5. Summarize what you have learned about social interaction on the Internet. What have you learned about intensive interviewing? What questions would you add, change, or delete in your interview schedule?

10 Multiple Methods in Context: Integration and Review

■ ■ ■ ■   Text Objectives

1. Identify the advantages of macro-level and micro-level research for answering particular research questions.

2. Design vignettes and questions for use in a factorial survey.

3. Interpret findings from a meta-analysis.

4. Explain the value of triangulation in research methods.

Research in the News

1. A story about residents of a block in Harlem generated a picture of a social context that offered little hope and few social supports for those seeking stable jobs and families (Felicia R. Lee, "On a Harlem Block, Hope Is Swallowed by Decay." *The New York Times*, September 8, 1994: A1, B8, B9). Drug dealing and drug and alcohol abuse were rampant, teenage pregnancies were common, education was often truncated, and fathers were often missing. Regular employment and romantic relationships were viewed by many as impossible, even deviant, goals.

How could this social context influence relationships between such variables as education, occupational mobility, social support, life satisfaction, criminal victimization, and religiosity? Would responses to any particular fixed-choice survey questions be particularly suspect in this context? What field research methods could be used to help to understand attitudes in this context? [360–361]

2. A contrasting social context was presented by a recent article on improving employment prospects (Judith H. Dobrzynski, "The New Jobs: A Growing Number Are Good Ones." *The New York Times*, July 21, 1996: F1, F10–F11 [corrected chart on July 28, 1996: 9]). Job opportunities are increasing, with increasingly good pay, it noted, in business, recreation, social, and brokerage services, as well as in nonbanking financial institutions. In cities with the fastest job growth, some job seekers report that the jobs they have been able to obtain exceed their expectations.

How could this social context influence relationships between such variables as education, occupational mobility, social support, life satisfaction, criminal victimization, and religiosity? Would responses to any particular fixed-choice survey questions be particularly suspect in this context? What field research methods could be used to help to understand attitudes in this context? [360–361]

Compare these answers to those you wrote for question 1. What methodological challenges would be confronted in an attempt to conduct comparable research in both of these social contexts? [364–369]

_____

_____

_____

_____

_____

_____

_____

_____

_____

_____

_____

_____

_____

_____

Short Essay Questions

1. Why triangulate? Review the strengths and weaknesses of experimental, survey, and field research as means of achieving measurement and causal validity and generalizability. Explain how methodological triangulation helps to achieve these goals. Give one example from the text. [355–360]

_____

_____

_____

_____

_____

_____

_____

_____

_____

_____

_____

_____

_____

_____

_____

_____

2. You must convince a survey researcher to add a qualitative component to a survey about ethnic conflict. The researcher already is short of the funds required to draw the type of sample he wants. Develop some persuasive arguments. You can buttress your arguments with examples from the text. [358–360]

_____

_____

_____

_____

_____

_____

_____

_____

_____

_____

_____

3. Describe a hypothetical meta-analysis of experimental studies of the effect of authoritarian leadership on conformity. Indicate measurement and sampling procedures. Conclude with a short essay on the features that make meta-analysis appealing but relatively uncommon. [361–363]

_____

_____

_____

_____

_____

_____

_____

_____

_____

_____

4. Select four of the 12 research design lessons (text pp. 364–368). Explain what they mean and why they are important. Illustrate each of the four lessons with an example from a study in the text. [364–369]

_____

_____

_____

_____

_____

_____

_____

_____

_____

_____

_____

_____

_____

_____

_____

_____

_____

_____

_____

_____

Mini-Projects

A Factorial Survey

Choose a current political issue or social problem as a focus for a short factorial survey.

1. Find a newspaper or magazine article that describes some situation or event. For example, the vignette might describe a situation in which there is pressure on the United States to intervene militarily in another country.

2. Identify some characteristic of the individuals or actions in the situation or event that you believe influenced the outcome—perhaps the political figure calling for action or the country against which military action is contemplated.

3. Write a vignette that captures this key characteristic of the situation or event. Then prepare a variant of the vignette in which you alter this characteristic of the situation or event. For example, substitute different political figures or different countries.

4. Add instructions and a few questions. For example, "Please read the following description of a recent event. Which of the following responses would you favor? How strongly do you feel about that?"

5. Administer the factorial survey to at least 10 students, either in a class or at cafeteria tables or in a group meeting. Distribute the two versions randomly (alternating one with the other).

6. Compare the average responses to the two versions of the vignettes. Discuss possible reasons for the differences or lack of differences. Review what you have learned about the factorial survey approach and propose several research problems for which it could be used.

Qualitative or Quantitative?

Focus this project on a favorite (or at least interesting) field research classic. Most of these are books, such as *Tally's Corner, Street Corner Society,* and *Jelly's Bar.*

1. Summarize the book's main points.

2. Search the literature for a survey or experimental study that focused on a research question that is similar to one that was the explicit or implicit focus of the field study.

3. Compare the quantitative study to the field research study, based on careful notes on both.

4. Write out a detailed comparison of the similarities and differences in the research question posed, the methods used, and the conclusions developed.

5. Conclude with an analysis of the advantages and disadvantages of the two methods for investigating the chosen research question.

Meta-Analysis Revisited

Extend exercise 2 (text p. 370) by refining your research question and coding scheme and coding more articles.

1. Identify five more research articles that tested the same hypothesis as selected for exercise 2.

2. Refine your coding scheme based on your prior coding. Add or delete study characteristics to more adequately represent the methods and findings of each study.

3. Code the five additional articles on the revised form. Recode any previously coded articles, if necessary, in light of the form revisions.

4. Calculate the cross-study mean (arithmetic average) percentages, and other statistics for those variables that appear in multiple studies.

5. Summarize the strength of any associations tested in more than one study.

6. Write up a description of your methods and findings.

11   **Data Analysis**

■   ■   ■   ■   **Text Objectives**

1. Identify features that enhance and diminish the clarity of graphic displays and frequency distributions.

2. Match different types of variables and research purposes with appropriate statistics.

3. Calculate or determine mode, median, mean, standard deviation, range, interquartile range, and standard deviation with ungrouped data.

4. Construct and interpret crosstabulations of two and three variables.

5. Use elaboration analysis to test for spurious, mediating, and conditional relationships.

6. Distinguish descriptive and inferential statistics.

Research in the News

1. You've probably heard it said that our schools are failing to provide students with an adequate education and that school standards have been declining in spite of greater spending. Maybe you know there have been numerous books in recent years making exactly this claim. But some "revisionist" social scientists have argued that the schools aren't on the decline after all (Peter Applebome, "Have Schools Failed? Revisionists Use Army of Statistics to Argue No." *The New York Times,* December 13, 1995: B16). They argue that SAT scores have declined because a larger proportion of high school students are taking them, not because performance is on the wane. They note that increased spending on schools has been largely to support special-needs education; therefore, it's no wonder that this spending did not result in better overall performance.

Sketch out several three-variable causal models in which student performance is the dependent variable and school spending is the independent variable. Posit several intervening, extraneous, and specifying variables in this relationship. [405–411]

2. A study by the Population Council found that rates of divorce and out-of-wedlock births have been rising since 1970 in many countries (Tamar Lewin, "Family Decay Global, Study Says." *The New York Times*, May 30, 1995: A5). Global changes in gender roles and the economic status of women seem to be driving these changes. Income levels, types of employment, education levels, and child-support policies are also cited as relevant.

If you had to describe the rates of divorce and other measures across societies, which statistics would you use? What concerns would you have about the appropriateness and comparability of different measures of central tendency and variability in these international comparisons? [389–398]

_____

_____

_____

_____

_____

_____

_____

_____

_____

_____

_____

Short Essay Questions

1. Discuss the advantages and disadvantages of the mode, the median, and the mean as measures of the central tendency of variables. [389–394]

_____

_____

_____

_____

_____

_____

_____

_____

_____

_____

_____

_____

2. Describe situations in which a variable's variability is best measured by the range, interquartile range, and standard deviation. When might the use of both the interquartile range and the standard deviation be fruitful? [394–398]

_____

_____

_____

_____

_____

_____

_____

3. Fifteen teenagers were asked how often they attended church in the preceding month. Their responses are: 0, 0, 4, 6, 1, 5, 5, 8, 2, 0, 1, 3, 3, 1, 9.

Determine the value of the mode, median, and mean for these numbers.
Describe the shape of the distribution. [389–394]

4. Describe the association between the two variables in table 11.1. [400–
403]

Table 11.1   **Level of Support for Eliminating AFDC by Education
(Hypothetical)**

| | Education | | |
Level of Support	Elementary School	High School	College
Very low	35%	20%	60%
Low	35	30	20
High	20	10	15
Very high	10	40	5
	100%	100%	100%
	(230)	(111)	(62)

5. Consider the variable "strength of anti-immigrant sentiment." With respect to what relationship between two other variables could it play the role of an intervenor? An extraneous variable? A specifier? Justify your selections and diagram your causal models. [405–411]

Multiple-Choice Questions

1. An economist reports on the rising level of consumer spending. He says that he can estimate the spending level at the 95% confidence level, and that his best guess is that it is up by 4.3. The numbers 95% and 4.3 are, respectively, _____. [374]

    a. both descriptive statistics
    b. inferential statistics, descriptive statistics
    c. both inferential statistics
    d. descriptive or inferential, depending on the context
    e. descriptive statistics, inferential statistics

2.

    In the diagram, "socializing" could be thought of as _____. [405–411]
    a. a causal mechanism
    b. an extraneous variable
    c. a confounding factor
    d. a spurious relationship
    e. a concomitant variable

3. Students report on a federal form the amount of their school expenses that they pay for out of their own pockets. The amounts are rounded to the nearest integer. What are the true limits of a rounded value of 572? [387]

    a. 571.0–572.0
    b. 565–575
    c. 571.9–572.9
    d. 571.5–572.5
    e. 572.0–572.9

4.

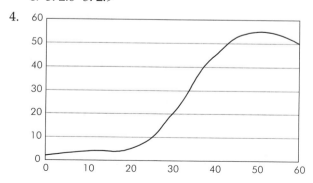

What will be the relation between the values of the mode, median, and mean in the distribution? [390–394]

    a. The mean will be lowest; the mode will be highest.
    b. The mean and median will be equal, and greater than the mode.
    c. The median and mode will be equal, and lower than the mean.
    d. The mean will be highest; the mode will be lowest.
    e. The median will be lowest; the median will be highest.

5. Number of cults in each of 13 states: 5, 12, 22, 7, 15, 22, 19, 14, 20, 18, 21, 13, 0. What is the median in the array of number of cults? [391–392]

    a. 18.5
    b. 18.0
    c. 14.0
    d. 19.0
    e. 22.5

6. Number of employees in each of eight shops: 32, 23, 22, 17, 46, 42, 5, 13. What is the mean in the array? [392]

    a. 22.5
    b. 40.0
    c. 40.5
    d. 200
    e. 41.0

7. What is the interquartile range in the following array of ages? 28, 52, 29, 37, 24, 50, 10, 33, 26, 35, 37, 40 [396–397]

    a. 21
    b. 42
    c. 11.5
    d. 8
    e. 43

8. What is the variance for the following array of the number of children taken care of by each of five family day care providers? 1, 1, 2, 3, 3 [397–398]

    a. .8
    b. 2.0
    c. 3.0
    d. 1.2
    e. .9

Table 11.2   **Family Cohesion By Job Insecurity of Family Head (Hypothetical Data)**

	Job Insecurity		
Cohesion	Low	Medium	High
Low	65%	65%	75%
Medium	15	20	15
High	20	15	10
Total	100%	100%	100%
N	(721)	(500)	(325)

9. In table 11.2, what percentage of the families whose head has a job with medium insecurity also have a low level of cohesion? [400–401]

    a. 50%

    b. 35%

    c. 45%

    d. 30%

    e. 20%

10. In table 11.2, which statement best describes the relationship?

    a. Family cohesion increases as job insecurity decreases.

    b. There is essentially no association between job insecurity and family cohesion.

    c. Family cohesion increases as job insecurity increases.

    d. As job insecurity increases, family cohesion decreases and then increases.

    e. As job insecurity increases, family cohesion increases and then decreases.

11. It is posited in a causal model that school performance influences social ties, which in turn influence depression. What does the model indicate will be true of the association between school performance and depression in the subtables after social ties are controlled, as well as of the bivariate relations between social ties, school performance, and depression? [400–411]

    a. There will be a bivariate association between school performance and depression, but there will be no association between them in the subtables.

    b. There will not be a bivariate association between school performance and depression, nor will there be an association between them in the subtables.

c. There will be a bivariate association between school performance and depression, but there will be an association between them in only one of the subtables.

d. There will be a bivariate association between school performance and depression, but the direction of this association will be reversed in the subtables.

e. There will be a bivariate association between school performance and depression, and there will also be an association between them in the subtables.

Mini-Projects

Professional Styles of Presentation

This project will help to increase your presentational repertoire.

1. Select five issues of at least two social science journals that present the results of original quantitative research.

2. Review each article in each issue. Focus your attention only on those articles that include tables presenting quantitative data.

3. Create a list for each journal issue that shows the total number of articles, the number of articles using quantitative data, and the number of data tables in each of these articles. For each table, record the statistics that were used and describe the format of the presentation.

4. Compare what you have found to the statistics and presentational options on text pp. 379–411. What additional presentational options have you encountered? Which do you prefer? Why? What additional statistics do you need to learn about in order to read this journal literature?

A Tertiary Data Analysis

The term "secondary data analysis" is applied to the analysis of previously collected data. If you redo someone's secondary data analysis, perhaps we can think of that as a "tertiary data analysis."

1. Identify several journal articles that present an analysis of General Social Survey data. (See the World Wide Web appendix in this study guide for one way to identify such articles or just use *Sociological Abstracts* in your library.)

2. Pick one article that presents at least some tables using statistics that you are now familiar with.

3. Read the article and list all GSS variables used in it. Compare this list to the list of variables in the 1994 General Social Survey dataset on your disk. Although the article is likely to have used an earlier or later year's version of the GSS, many of the variables are measured each time. If many of the variables match, you're in business. If not, try to find another article for this assignment.

4. Now work out the SPSS commands you will use to replicate the article's analysis with your own analysis using the 1994 GSS data.

5. Conduct your reanalysis. Be sure to periodically save your SPSS syntax file as you work and to either print out or save on disk the output you generate.

6. Compare your findings to those in the journal article. Discuss the similarities and differences. Propose an explanation for each of the differences you found, considering the different years involved, any changes in the measures, and chance variation.

Reviewing the Possibilities

Focus your attention on a relationship between two variables that has been found in prior research. Studies presented in the text can be the source of the relationship.

1. List possible variables that might be involved in this relationship as *extraneous, intervening,* or *specifying.*

2. After identifying several such possibilities, search the literature to try to find one study that relates to each of these possibilities. For example, if you expect that the association between broken homes and delinquency is spurious due to the effect of social class, try to find a study of the broken homes–delinquency relationship in which social class was controlled. Alternatively, a study showing that social class was related to either broken homes or delinquency would provide some support for the proposition that social class created a spurious association.

3. Review the evidence you have found and then identify the three-variable relationship that received the most support.

4. Write a brief report on efforts to elaborate on the relationship on which you focused.

Exploring the General Social Survey

1. Review the list of variables I used in the analysis of voting in the 1988 presidential election (Exhibit 11.2, text p. 377). Each of these variables reappears in the 1994 GSS, although VOTE92 has been substituted for VOTE88. Our goal is to see if the analysis of likelihood of voting in the 1988 election between Bush and Dukakis can be replicated for the 1992 election between Bush and Clinton. [377–500]

2. Practice graphing with SPSS. Again, just try to replicate what I presented from the 1991 GSS. You can use the pull-down graphics menu or run the following commands in the SPSS syntax window. [512–515]

```
FRE MARSTAT/FORMAT=NOTABLE/BARCHART.
FRE POLVIEWS/FORMAT=NOTABLE/HISTOGRAM.
GRAPH/LINE(SIMPLE)=COUNT BY EDUC.
```

3. Compare the percentage who voted in 1988 (Exhibit 11.8, text p. 386) and the distribution of political views in 1988 (Exhibit 11.9, text p. 387) with the corresponding percentages in the 1994 GSS. You can also generate some measures of central tendency and variability for political views. [512–515]

```
RECODE VOTE92(3,4=9).
```

[This removes from the analysis the cases that were not eligible to vote or refused to answer, since 9 is declared as a missing value.]

```
FRE VOTE92.
FRE POLVIEWS/STATS=MEAN,MEDIAN,STDDEV.
```

4. Now replicate the recoding of the age distribution. First inspect the unrecoded distribution and then use a recode statement to generate a distribution categorized as in Exhibit 11.10 (text p. 388). [512–515]

```
FRE AGE/FORMAT=ONEPAGE.
RECODE AGE(18,19=1)(20 THRU 29=2)(30 THRU 39=3)....
VALUE LABELS AGE 1 '18-19' 2 '20-29' 3 '30-39' ....
FRE AGE.
```

5. Do the same with the distribution of education (see Exhibit 11.12, text p. 390). [512–515]

```
FRE EDUC.
RECODE EDUC (0 THRU 7=1)(8 THRU 11=2)(12=3)(13
    THRU 15=4)(16=5)(17 THRU HI=6).
VALUE LABELS EDUC 1 'LESS THAN 8' 2 '8-11'....
FRE EDUC.
```

6. To examine the effect of skew on the location of the mean and median (text pp. 379–380), convert the values of the RINCOM91 variable to the dollar midpoints of each category. That will give them numerical values that correspond to the actual dollar ranges that they represent. (For example, the value 2, which represents $1,000–2,999, would be recoded to 1999.5.) Use 0 as the starting point of category 1 and 100,000 as the ending point of category 21. Also recode the value 22, which means "refused," to 98 (so it becomes missing).

Now calculate the mean, the median, and the mode.

```
FRE RINCOM91/HISTOGRAM/STATS=MEAN,MEDIAN,MODE.
```

Inspect the graph of income and comment on its skew and the effect of that skew on the relative values of the mean, median, and mode. [513–514]

7. Now you are to replicate the crosstabular analysis of VOTE88, using VOTE92. This analysis is represented in Exhibits 11.18 to 11.21 and Exhibits 11.23 to 11.28 (text pp. 401–411). Reread the discussion of this analysis before you start. [515–518]

```
RECODE INCOME91(1 THRU 10=1)(11 THRU 15=2)(16 THRU
    18=3)(19 THRU 21=4).
VALUE LABELS INCOME91 1 'LT 15,000' 2 '15-29999'
    3 '....
CROSSTABS VOTE92 BY INCOME91/CELLS=COUNT,COL.
RECODE AGE (LO THRU 29=1)(30 THRU 39=2)....
VALUE LABELS AGE 1 'LT 30' 2 '30-39' 3....
CROSSTABS VOTE92 BY AGE/CELLS=COUNT,ROW.
CROSSTABS VOTE92 BY ANOMIA7,SEX/CELLS=COUNT,COL.
CROSSTABS ANOMIA7 BY INCOME91/CELLS=COUNT,COL.
CROSSTABS ANOMIA7 BY INCOME92 BY
    ANOMIA7/CELLS=COUNT,COL.
RECODE EDUC (0 THRU 11=1)(12=2)(13 THRU HI=3).
CROSSTABS VOTE92 BY EDUC/INCOME91 BY
    EDUC/CELLS=COUNT,COL.
```

```
CROSSTABS VOTE92 BY INCOME91 BY
    EDUC/CELLS=COUNT,COL.
CROSSTABS VOTE92 BY INCOME91 BY
    RACE/CELLS=COUNT,COL.
```

8. Summarize the relationship in each table and compare it to that found in the corresponding text table. What have you learned about stability and change in patterns of participation in the two presidential elections? What additional research questions are suggested? [400–411]

12 Reporting Research Results

■ ■ ■ ■ **Text Objectives**

1. Prepare combined and compressed data displays.

2. Organize and write a research report that would be of use to a social agency or other organization.

3. Define *scientific paradigm* and explain its role in scientific revolutions.

4. Explain the constructivist paradigm and contrast it to the research circle.

5. List arguments for and against participatory action research.

Research in the News

1. A survey on voter participation resulted in the surprising conclusion that nonvoters are no more alienated than voters (Richard L. Berke, "Nonvoters Are No More Alienated Than Voters, a Survey Shows." *The New York Times*, May 30, 1996: A21). Conducted by a Democratic and a Republican polling organization working together, the survey found that nonvoters didn't see voting as particularly important, but they were no more mistrustful of government than were voters. There were some differences: Nonvoters felt it less likely than voters that their vote would make a difference, and they didn't see as much difference between the two major political parties.

Propose a participatory or a constructivist research approach to learn more about what influences the propensity to vote. Focus your proposal on working with a nonpartisan "get-out-the-vote" organization. Explain how you would approach the group and what types of activities you would engage in during your research that would reflect your participatory or constructivist stance. [432–435]

2. New Yorkers must have felt pleased to learn in a 1995 *Times* article about a decline in the rate of violent crime (Clifford Krauss, "New York Sees Steepest Decline in Violent Crime Rate Since '72." *The New York Times*, December 31, 1995: 1, 32). Possible causes cited were a more active policing strategy, a focus on gang prosecutions, gang peace pacts, longer prison sentences, and an aging population.

You are beginning a study of neighborhood crime watch groups and hope to learn more about how members perceive the risk of crime. You discuss your research with friends and soon find yourself immersed in arguments about the appropriate goals for your research. Draft arguments that might have been used to try to persuade you to adopt, as your research goals, advancing scientific knowledge, shaping social policy, organizing social action, and dialoguing with research subjects. What are the points of compatibility and of conflict between these various goals? How would you respond to them? [428–435]

Short Essay Questions

1. When can political goals legitimately shape social research? When a research problem is defined? While a research project is being carried out? When the report is prepared? Evaluate each possibility and weigh the positive and negative impacts of your decisions on the goal of achieving valid research findings. [428–435]

_____

_____

_____

_____

_____

_____

_____

_____

_____

_____

_____

_____

_____

_____

_____

2. Is the review process for journal articles a model of how to maximize the quality of scientific publications? Compare and contrast that model to the way in which research reports are likely to be reviewed. What are the elements in both processes that are most likely to interfere with maximizing publication quality? What means would you suggest to minimize the impact of these elements? [437–441]

_____

_____

_____

_____

_____

_____

_____

_____

_____

_____

_____

_____

_____

_____

_____

_____

_____

3. What are the major problems that you confront in writing research or other course papers? List these problems and identify those that you have encountered most often in your writing. Present a plan for overcoming these problems. [428–435]

_____

_____

_____

_____

_____

_____

_____

_____

_____

_____

_____

_____

_____

_____

4. Is tactical research ever legitimate? What indicators could be used to identify a survey project as involving this approach? How can tactical survey research be distinguished from legitimate research by political pollsters and marketing firms? [437–438]

_____

_____

_____

_____

_____

_____

_____

_____

_____

_____

5. The following table is based on a compressed table I prepared for a report on clients in some local service programs. Write a brief verbal description of the characteristics of clients in these programs. To what extent are the clients similar across programs with respect to these characteristics? Could these different client mixes have influenced the effect of prior education on ability to secure employment? Explain your answer. [445–448]

_____

_____

_____

_____

_____

Table 12.1 **Client Characteristics in Six Service Programs**

	Percent Female	Percent Af-Am	Percent Hispanic	Percent English Speaking	Mean Age	Total Clients
Program 1	42%	54%	10%	84%	42.16	125
Program 2	100%	20%	0	100%	34.4	57
Program 3	100%	43%	0	100%	40.11	63
Program 4	67%	17%	0	100%	38.33	600
Program 5	93%	62%	8%	100%	49.15	11
Program 6	100%	17%	33%	100%	34.83	76
Total	**62%**	**48%**	**10%**	**91%**	**41.49**	**932**

Multiple-Choice Questions

1. A researcher conducts a study of student involvement in campus politics. He identifies different interest groups, interviews members of these different groups, talks with interviewees about the issues raised by other interviewees, and attempts to reach consensus on issues about which there is disagreement. The research exemplifies _____. [431–439]

    a. tactical research
    b. normal science
    c. participatory action research
    d. the constructivist paradigm
    e. social science as public philosophy

Table 12.2 **Support for Alternative Criminal Justice Policies (Hypothetical Data)**

Policy	Support	Neutral	Oppose	Total
3 strikes and you're out	12%	14	74	100% (57)
Parole impossible	40%	31	29	100% (62)
Victim at sentencing	21%	31	48	100% (58)
No juvenile court	12%	3	85	100% (55)

2. Table 12.2 is a _____. [446]

    a. crosstabulation
    b. combined frequency display
    c. subtable
    d. compressed display
    e. frequency distribution

3. Which of the following statements is consistent with the data displayed in table 12.2? [445–448]

    a. "Three strikes and you're out" is the most popular policy.
    b. Respondents tend to support special treatment for juveniles.
    c. Of those who strongly oppose current criminal justice policies, 48% are against allowing victims' perspectives to be represented at sentencing.
    d. The relationship between support for alternative policies and criminal justice policies is curvilinear.
    e. Making parole impossible is less popular than victim representation at sentencing.

Table 12.3 **Political Beliefs by Education (Hypothetical Data)**

%Believe	Education		
	Elementary School	High School	College
Pro-life	40% (157)	25% (243)	19% (76)
Victim rights	12% (141)	15% (217)	14% (45)
Equitable taxes	27% (158)	22% (241)	12% (77)
Longer sentences	34% (150)	21% (232)	19% (71)

4. Table 12.3 is a _____. [446]

    a. crosstabulation

    b. combined frequency display

    c. subtable

    d. compressed display

    e. frequency distribution

5. Which of the following statements is consistent with the data displayed in table 12.3? [447–448]

    a. Support for victim rights has a positive monotonic association with education.

    b. Elementary school is the modal education category.

    c. Support for longer sentences decreases with education.

    d. Support for victim rights was the most contentious issue.

    e. There is no association between education and support for equitable taxes.

Mini-Projects

Research Report Standards

You will need to make some calls to find a local research organization that produces publicly available research reports. A good bet would be your campus survey research center, if your school has one.

1. Obtain one or more research reports from the organization.

2. For an extra effort, interview the report's author, or one of its authors. Inquire about the pressures experienced and the decisions made in crafting the report.

3. Read the report and inspect carefully its tables and charts. Answer each of the pertinent questions in Exhibit 6.1, "Questions to Ask about a Research Article" (text pp. 192–193).

4. Suggest improvements in the tables, charts, and associated text.

5. Speculate, based on the available evidence, on the extent to which the report was written with a goal of advancing science, shaping policy, organizing action, or dialoguing with subjects. How are these goals reflected in the contents of the report? Did the consequences of nonscientific goals include interference with achieving the goal of validity? What advice would you give the authors of the next such report?

A Constructivist Inquiry

Conduct a constructivist inquiry about student reactions to your college, university, or graduate program.

1. Select individuals in a class, residential house, or some particular club to serve as the project's focus.

2. Interview a series of people in the chosen group or setting, in a serial fashion so that later interviewees are identified by referrals from earlier interviewees, and so that the content of your questions develops as you learn more about student reactions.

3. Continue interviewing until you have conducted at least five interviews. Then reinterview one of your first respondents.

4. Write up your notes each day after you complete an interview.

5. Write a report on what you have learned about student reactions. Conclude with a discussion about the extent to which constructivist inquiry aids or hinders attaining valid conclusions.

Exploring the General Social Survey

1. Present the variables measuring confidence in institutions in a combined frequency display. Include appropriate labels, titles, and footnotes. The display will be improved if you organize the variables into logical subgroups or in the order of diminishing confidence. Describe the level of confidence in these institutions. [512–515]

```
FRE CONFINAN TO CONARMY.
```

_____

_____

_____

_____

_____

_____

_____

_____

_____

_____

_____

_____

_____

2. Create a compressed crosstabular display to show the relationship between gender and attitudes toward gender roles. Just present the percentage who "agree" with each statement in the body of the table. Indicate the number of valid cases for each variable in the table's margin. Label the table and all its rows and columns. [518]

```
CROSSTABS FEHOME TO FEPOL BY SEX/CELLS=COUNT,COL.
```

Resources for Research on the World Wide Web

Government Resources*

Government Documents

`http://www.lib.umich.edu/libhome/documents`

The most general starting point for finding all types of government resources, including publications, statistics, and funding opportunities. Includes links to many nongovernment sources. Can be searched by discipline.

Federal Legislation

`http://thomas.loc.gov`

Information on pending and past legislation, committee composition.

Federal Publications

`http://www.fedworld.gov/index.html`

National Technical Information Service source for ordering government publications.

National Institutes of Health

`http://www.nih.gov/`

Information about programs and grants.

General Sites for Linking to Social Science Resources

`http://www.w3.org/hypertext/datasources/bysubject/`
`sociology/overview.html`

Links to research centers, departments of sociology, discussion groups, electronic journals, and other resources.

`http://www.sonic.net/~markbl/socioweb/`

Various resources for those interested in sociology, including a guide to graduate programs, Web search engines, and professional associations.

---

* Please note: Web addresses and home pages change periodically. Don't be surprised to find new content at some of the listed sites or to find that some of these sites no longer exist.

`http://www.carleton.ca/~cmckie/research.html`

Other social science search lists, data archives, reference materials, and case studies for sociology courses.

`http://sosig.ac.uk/welcome.html`

Links to resources in sociology, research methods, and other social sciences. Professional associations, data sources, academic departments, mailing lists, and research centers.

`http://www.trinity.edu/~mkearl/index.html`

Links to many resources, including government statistics, data sources, and theory groups.

`http://www.princeton.edu/~sociolog/links.html`

Other search aids, lists of professional associations, sociology departments, university catalogs, and data archives.

`http://osiris.colorado.edu/soc/links.html`

More links to sociology resources.

Library Resources

`http://www.uakron.edu/hefe/lib1.html`

Library of Congress, presidential libraries, database of academic research journals, and academic libraries with Web servers.

`http://www.carl.org/uncover/unchome.html`

Bibliographic database with 17,000 periodicals indexed, online article delivery service.

`http://www.socabs.org`

Information on *Sociological Abstracts,* with search service available to subscribers only.

`http://www.ref.oclc.org:2000/`

Access to FirstSearch online bibliography and to electronic journals. Available only through libraries.

http://www.annurev.org/soc/home.htm

Annual Review of Sociology online. Abstracts from all 22 volumes can be searched by concept or keyword. Complete articles can be downloaded for $5 per article.

http://nch.ari.net

National Coalition for the Homeless. Online library that can be searched for references to reports on homelessness. Includes facts and figures, legislative developments, recordings of homeless people describing their experiences, and a directory of organizations.

http://www.nytimes.com

The New York Times Web edition, with regular news stories and other regular newspaper sections. Some pictures and audio files. Also: special news sections for Web users; online forums, allowing you to read comments on an issue—and to send a comment yourself; and search options.

http://popindex.princeton.edu/

Population Index for 1986–1996.

http://olympus.lang.arts.ualberta.ca:8010/

Electronic Journal of Sociology. Full text of articles published only online.

http://www.socresonline.org.uk/socresonline/

Sociological Research Online. Full text articles published only online.

Datasets and Research Resources

General Social Survey

http://www.icpsr.umich.edu/gss/

Search all years of the GSS for variables of interest. Check wording of questions and response choices, see frequency distributions for variables in different sets of years, obtain list of GSS publications, and download GSS datasets.

U.S. Census

http://ftp.census.gov/

The U.S. Census Bureau homepage. Contains tables and graphs reporting detailed census data. Population data and economic indicators.

U.S. Census Zip Code Files

http://ftp.census.gov/geo/www/gazetteer/places.html

Provides files for downloading that contain information on counties and zip code areas, including state code, population, housing units, land area, and latitude and longitude.

http://www.psc.lsa.umich.edu/ssdan/

Source of census data in tabular format ready for student analysis. Requires StudentCHIP software, available for $5.

U.S. Postal Service

http://www.usps.gov/

Look up zip codes corresponding to street addresses. Useful for survey mailings.

http://www.fbi.gov/ucrpress.htm

Written summary of the FBI's Uniform Crime Reports.

Department of Labor, Bureau of Labor Statistics

http://stats.bls.gov

Statistical reports, bibliographies, and descriptions of ongoing surveys. Time-series data available for downloading.

Panel Study of Income Dynamics

http://www.umich.edu/~psid

Data sets and related information available from longitudinal study of U.S. individuals and families that began in 1968.

National Election Survey

http://www.umich.edu/~nes

Includes responses to questions asked since 1952, test of 1996 NES questionnaire, and data for online analysis. Searchable by keyword.

Gallup Poll

http://www.gallup.com
Poll results and information on current events.

The Roper Center

http://www.lib.uconn.edu/ropercenter/
General information on the Roper Center.

Answers

Multiple-Choice Questions

Chapter 1
1. a 2. e 3. d 4. b 5. a 6. a

Chapter 2
1. b 2. d 3. d 4. d 5. b 6. a 7. d 8. d 9. a

Chapter 3
1. c 2. b 3. b 4. b 5. a 6. d 7. b 8. c 9. a 10. b 11. e 12. c 13. a

Chapter 4
1. b 2. e 3. c 4. d 5. a 6. e 7. b 8. b 9. a 10. a

Chapter 5
1. a 2. a 3. b 4. e 5. a 6. c 7. c 8. c 9. b 10. c 11. c 12. e 13. b

Chapter 7
1. e 2. b 3. d 4. c 5. c 6. e 7. a 8. e 9. b 10. e 11. a

Chapter 8
1. c 2. c 3. b 4. c 5. e 6. a 7. c 8. c 9. d 10. a

Chapter 9
1. d 2. b 3. d 4. c

Chapter 11
1. b 2. a 3. d 4. a 5. b 6. b 7. c 8. e 9. a 10. c 11. a

Chapter 12
1. d 2. b 3. a 4. d 5. c